American Girl®
W9-AXX-136
The Quiz Book
Can you keep a secret?
Are you ready for a pet?
How silly are you?
Are you a true friend?
Clues to You & Your Friends, Too!

American Girl®

The Quiz Book

Clues to You & Your Friends, Too!

By Laura Allen

Illustrated by Debbie Tilley

American Girl®

Dear Reader,

Are you a **happy camper?** How **silly** are you? Can you keep a **secret?** Find out by taking **quizzes** that reveal these and many more clues about you.

You'll **discover** who you are today and who you may become in the future. Just remember that as you grow, your **feelings** and **thoughts** change, too. Your answers today may be different tomorrow!

So sharpen your pencil and gather friends and family around. Get set to **learn** a little—and **laugh** a lot!

Your friends at American Girl

Contents

What's Your Style?

Are you **easygoing, soft** and **sweet,** or **bold** and **trendy?**
Circle the letter next to the answer that describes you best.

1. If you could buy a new beach towel, it would most likely have . . .

a. your favorite team's logo.

b. a colorful floral pattern.

c. big, bold stripes or shapes.

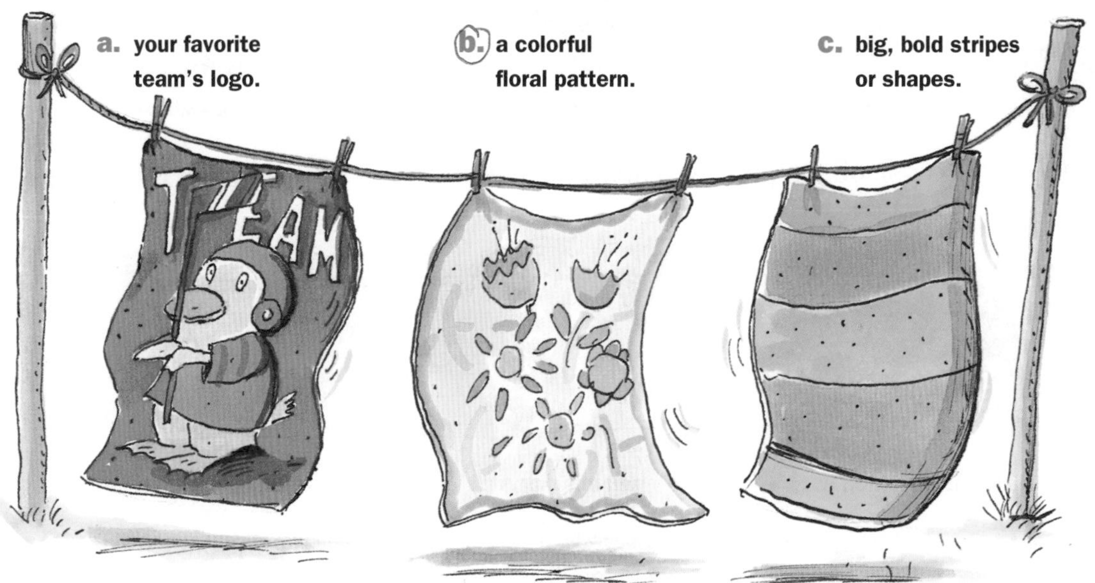

2. Your favorite hair accessory is . . .

a. a hairbrush.

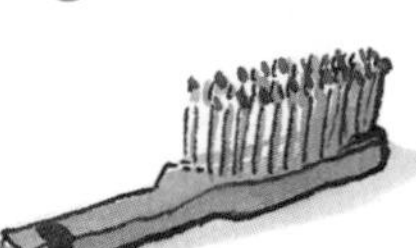

b. a velvet headband.

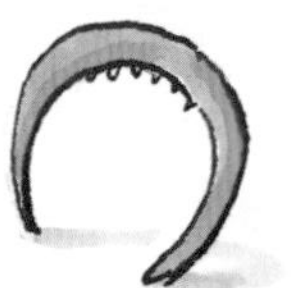

c. a butterfly clip.

3. Of these bracelets, your favorite would be . . .

a. a friendship bracelet your best friend made for you.

b. a charm bracelet.

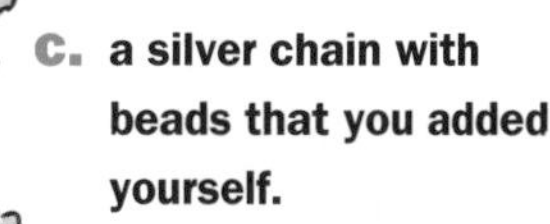

c. a silver chain with beads that you added yourself.

4. The hairstyle you like best is . . .
b. French braids.
a. short and easy.
c. the same cut that my favorite TV star has.
5. Your favorite hat is . . .
a. a baseball cap.
b. a straw sun hat.
c. a floppy black velvet hat.
A
6. If you were invited to a costume party, you'd most likely go as . . .
a. a cowgirl.
b. a medieval princess.
c. a hippie.

7. Your favorite shoes are . . .

a. sneakers.

b. strappy sandals.

c. black oxfords with chunky soles.

8. You sleep in . . .

a. a big T-shirt and sweatpants.

b. a nightgown.

c. PJ top and bottoms with a fun pattern.

Answers

Mostly a's

You're into what is comfy, casual, or sporty. You have a breezy, easygoing style.

Mostly b's

Pretty things make you smile. Your style is soft and sweet with a touch of glamour.

Mostly c's

Bold and trendy describes your style. You're often the first to try out the latest look.

Are You a Snoop?

Does your **nose** go where it's not **supposed** to go?
Circle the letter next to the answer that fits you best.

1. While looking for a book at the library, you hear two classmates in the next row whispering. You keep very quiet and try to listen to what they're saying.

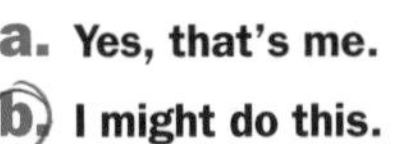

a. Yes, that's me.
b. I might do this.
c. I'd never do this.

2. When you use the rest room at your piano teacher's house, you peek into the cabinet behind the mirror to see what's there.

a. Yes, that's me.
b. I might do this.
c. I'd never do this.

3. While sharpening a pencil at your dad's desk at home, you see a letter to Aunt Doris on his computer screen. You read it.

a. Yes, that's me.
b. I might do this.
c. I'd never do this.

4. You're in the hall closet looking for a box to wrap your mom's holiday present in when you stumble on a huge shopping bag from Toy Town. You peek inside.

a. Yes, that's me.
b. I might do this.
c. I'd never do this.

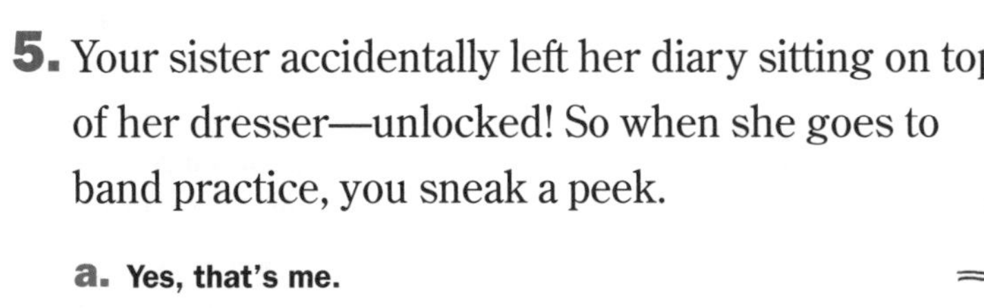

5. Your sister accidentally left her diary sitting on top of her dresser—unlocked! So when she goes to band practice, you sneak a peek.

a. **Yes, that's me.**
b. **I might do this.**
c. **I'd never do this.**

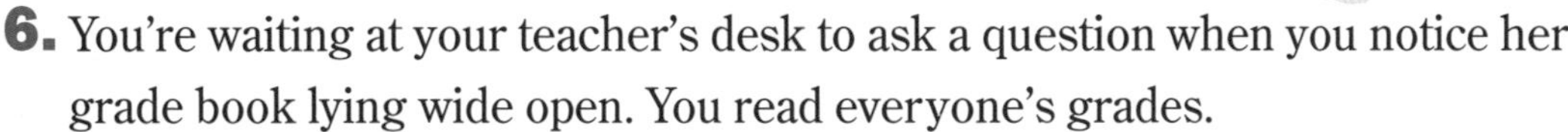

6. You're waiting at your teacher's desk to ask a question when you notice her grade book lying wide open. You read everyone's grades.

a. **Yes, that's me.**
b. **I might do this.**
c. **I'd never do this.**

7. You see two girls passing a note in class and giggling. Later on, you see the note crumpled up in the garbage. You fish it out to read it.

a. **Yes, that's me.**
b. **I might do this.**
c. **I'd never do this.**

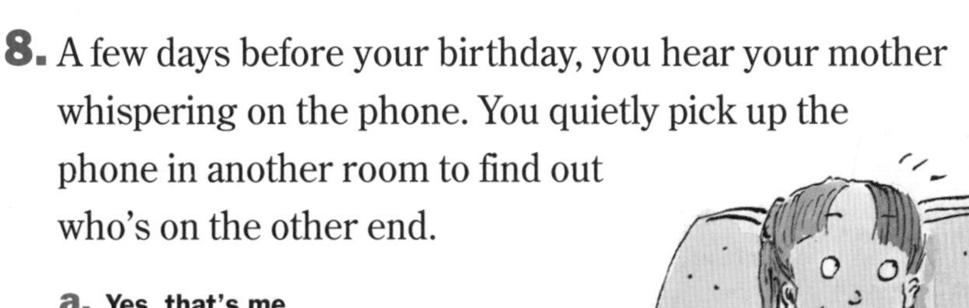

8. A few days before your birthday, you hear your mother whispering on the phone. You quietly pick up the phone in another room to find out who's on the other end.

a. **Yes, that's me.**
b. **I might do this.**
c. **I'd never do this.**

Answers

If you answered **a** more than once . . .

Too Snoopy

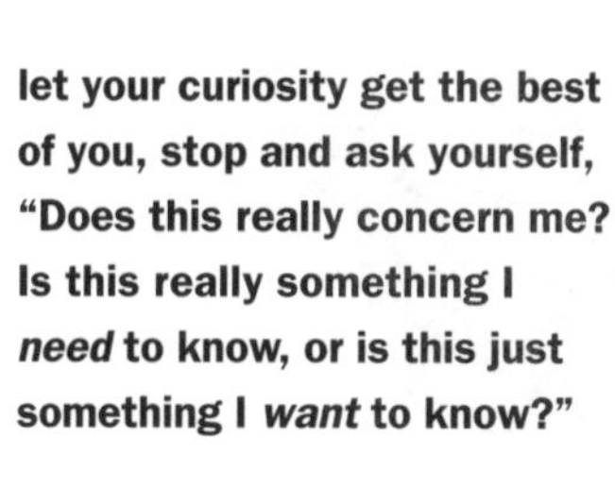

You may need to learn where to draw the line between what's your business and what isn't. Respecting other people's privacy is important, and it makes you someone they can trust. So before you let your curiosity get the best of you, stop and ask yourself, "Does this really concern me? Is this really something I *need* to know, or is this just something I *want* to know?"

Mostly **b**'s

Sometime Spy

You know it's not right to pry, but you just can't help yourself sometimes. Next time something private catches your eye, stop and listen to your conscience. Chances are that uneasiness you feel means you're sticking your nose where it doesn't belong.

Mostly **c**'s

Snoop Free

You don't let your eyes wander around to find gossip or to satisfy your curiosity. What's more, because others have learned that they can count on you to know what's your business and what's not, they respect you and often trust you with their secrets.

Tickled Pink or Feeling Blue?

Study the **colors** below and **pick** the one that you think **matches** your **mood** today. Then turn the page to see what some experts believe that **color** says about you.

Answers

Red

You're full of energy today. You're ready to go after a goal, ace a test, or just make each moment its best.

Yellow

You're feeling cheerful and bright. You may be looking ahead to future adventures or a fun escape.

Blue

You're in a thoughtful, mellow mood. You're seeking a quiet place to hang out in today.

Green

You're anxious and eager for others to recognize something special you've done.

Purple

Passionate and creative describes you right now. You're letting your heart rule your head.

Black

You're strong, determined, and perhaps a little reckless at heart today. You may even feel the need to make a change and give yourself a fresh start.

Pink

You're feeling kind and playful, spreading smiles and laughter wherever you go today.

Show Time!

Are you **on time** or **late for the show?** Circle the letter next to the answer that describes you best.

1. When it's time to get up for school, you . . .
   - **a. jump right out of bed.**
   - **b. lie there for five more dreamy minutes, then get up.**
   - **c. fall back asleep until Dad throws open the door to your room, opens the blinds, and yells, "Get up, sleepyhead!"**

2. As you get ready for school, you . . .
   - **a. keep a close eye on the time.**
   - **b. glance at a clock once or twice.**
   - **c. never check the time—Mom tells you when it's time to go.**

3. Your watch is set . . .
   - **a. five minutes fast.**
   - **b. on the dot.**
   - **c. What watch?**

4. When you arrive at the bus stop, you're . . .
   - **a. the first one there.**
   - **b. right on time.**
   - **c. the last one to show up.**

5. You have a soccer game after school, so you . . .
   - **a. go straight to the soccer field from school. You want to practice before the others arrive.**
   - **b. go straight home from school to get ready. You arrive at the field just in time for warm-up.**
   - **c. go home after school to watch your favorite cartoon and get ready during commercials. When your show is over, you rush to the field in time for the first whistle.**

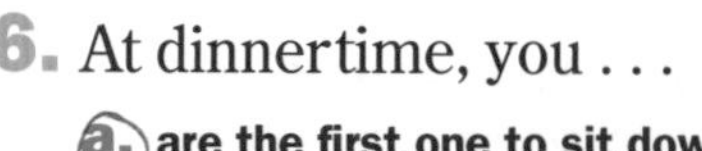

6. At dinnertime, you . . .

- **(a.) are the first one to sit down at the table.**
- **b. get there just as everyone else is sitting down.**
- **c. usually hear someone shout, "Your food is getting cold!"**

7. When a friend and her mom drive over to pick you up, you're . . .

- **(a.) ready and waiting on the front steps.**
- **b. putting your coat on and peeking out the window as they pull up.**
- **c. yelling, "Hey Mom! Where's my other shoe?"**

8. When you go to see a movie, you . . .

- **(a.) get there early so you can sit anywhere.**
- **b. arrive just in time to get a decent seat.**
- **c. stumble around in the dark and end up sitting in the front row.**

Answers

Mostly a's
Previews

You make it a point to be early. You don't want to miss out on anything—especially if you're competing for the best seat in the house!

Mostly b's
Show Time

Your mind tends to run like clockwork. You have a good sense of time and can get to where you're going without breaking a sweat.

Mostly c's
Excuse Me...

You probably lose track of time often. Try to plan ahead and keep your eye on the clock. And if your lateness just can't be helped, call ahead to let someone know.

S.S. Friendship

Can you **steer clear** of **friendship trouble?**
Take this quiz to find out.

1. You and Ali made plans to go to the library, but now Zoe asks you to go miniature golfing. You love mini golf, so you call Ali and tell her you're sick.

a. **Yes, that's me.** **b.** **I might do this.** **c.** **I'd never do this.**

2. You get into an argument with your friend Lisa because you think she stole your best babysitting job. As long as you're arguing, you bring up the time she borrowed your barrette and "forgot" to return it.

a. **Yes, that's me.** **b.** **I might do this.** **c.** **I'd never do this.**

3. At recess, your friend is wearing a new, super-insulated, bright-white winter coat. When a couple of classmates start teasing her and calling her a marshmallow, you can't resist joining in on the fun.

a. **Yes, that's me.** **b.** **I might do this.** **c.** **I'd never do this.**

4. You and Dana have been friends forever. But when Dana's not around and your new friends make fun of her, you go along with them.

a. **Yes, that's me.** **b.** **I might do this.** **c.** **I'd never do this.**

5. Your new friend has been hogging you. In fact, you can't do anything with anyone else without her expecting to be included. So you avoid her at school and tell your other friends to keep any plans you make with them a secret.

a. Yes, that's me. **b.** I might do this. **(c)** I'd never do this.

6. Your two best friends have started doing things without you. First it was the movies, then the mall, now the skating rink. You want to ask why, but you're afraid they'll say they don't like you anymore. So you say nothing and wait it out.

a. Yes, that's me. **(b)** I might do this. **c.** I'd never do this.

Answers

If you answered **a** or **b** more than once, you may need to learn how to keep your friendships out of icy waters.

1. Always stay true to your word and honor the first plan you made. When you start fibbing to a friend to take advantage of a better offer, you're headed for trouble!

2. Stick to the issue that upset you today. When you restart old arguments, you take everyone's attention away from what you need to talk about right now.

3. Teasing is usually only fun for the teaser. Joking about something that could embarrass a friend or hurt her feelings is downright cruel. Unless you want to spring a leak in a good friendship, don't do it.

4. Being two-faced can damage your friendship and your reputation. Be respectful of your friend's feelings whether she's present or not.

5. If you just avoid your friend, she's not going to get the right message. You need to tell her just how you feel: you value her friendship, but that doesn't mean you want to spend all your time with her.

6. If you care about your friendships, you owe it to your friends and yourself to at least talk about feeling excluded and find out what's going on.

Are You a Happy Camper?

Find out if you're too **careful** or too **carefree.**
Circle the letter next to the answer that describes you best.

1. It's the night before you leave for camp. As you lie in bed, you . . .

2. As you get ready to take your swimming test in the lake, you . . .

a. get a stomach ache. You're sure your legs will get tangled in that green stuff floating in the water.

b. get a little nervous about the water being too cold. You keep a sweatshirt nearby in case you get the shivers after your swim.

c. hope that this isn't going to take long so you can go back to the cabin and write your first letter home.

3. Your swim test lands you in the advanced class! The first thing you do is . . .

a. think it was a mistake and talk to a camp counselor about being put in the less advanced class where you'll feel safer.

(b.) see who else got into that class. Then find out if they're as nervous as you about learning lifesaving.

c. sign up to learn to water-ski on one ski—since you're finally qualified to try that.

4. You wake up with a bug bite that itches a lot. Your friends tell you it's a mosquito bite. You . . .

a. are not so sure. After all, you've been eyeing a big spider up in the corner of your cabin. Keep checking it. By lunchtime decide to go see the nurse.

(b.) slather on the calamine lotion and promise yourself you'll go to the nurse if it's not better by tomorrow.

c. put on some anti-itch cream and head out for fun without giving it a second thought.

5. You've all gathered at the flagpole for a daylong hike. You're the one . . .

a. wearing white gook on your nose, a hat, bug repellent, sunscreen, and a backpack weighed down with a first aid kit and a rain poncho.

(b.) who remembered to wear and pack sunscreen, fill a canteen, and bring a snack. Still, you feel that you may be missing something, so you check your backpack one more time.

c. without sunscreen or even a hat. You figure you'll be fine. Besides, if you start to burn, you can always borrow someone else's sunscreen.

6. Tonight your group is camping out. You've just heard a ghost story and climbed into your sleeping bag. Now as the firelight casts shadows across your tent, the wind whistles through the trees, and an owl hoots, you . . .

a. are convinced that a ghost or monster is going to get you.

b. worry about bears but then remind yourself that the fire should keep them away—as long as the counselors stay up long enough to keep it lit. Hmmm . . .

c. feel kind of thrilled about being frightened and think about how it's moments like these that make camp so great.

7. Your friends want to raid the boys' camp. You're sure that if you do it, you'll . . .

a. get chased by the boys and sprain your ankle trying to run away. You try to talk your friends out of it.

b. get into trouble unless you do it right. You come up with a plan to pull off the raid without getting caught.

c. have tons of fun. You can't wait to get going. Is it dark enough yet?

8. On the last night of camp, everyone puts on a show. You and the girls in your cabin have worked out a skit. Now you're . . .

a. wishing you weren't in it. You're sure you'll forget your lines or trip onstage.

b. a little nervous, so you ask a friend to help you rehearse your lines.

c. wishing someone had a video camera to record your stellar performance.

Answers

Mostly a's

Camp Oh-My-Gosh

The good news is you have a really active imagination. The bad news is that you tend to use it to spot potential dangers. It's important to think and plan ahead, but it's not good to fill yourself with dread. If you want to be a happier camper, think about the great things that could happen too!

Mostly b's

Camp Okee-Dokee

You worry a little but know when to stop. In fact, you know that there is a difference between getting yourself prepared and making yourself scared. So you try not to let your fears run away with you. Instead, you prepare just enough and then spend the rest of the time having fun.

Mostly c's

Camp What-Me-Worry?

You don't worry about events or stop to consider what could go wrong. You just enjoy doing things as they come along. This may work out well for you most of the time. But if you want to be a truly happy camper, think ahead a little more so you'll be prepared if trouble arises.

How Do You Doodle?

Are you a **shy sketcher** or a **daring designer?**
Find out what your doodles say about you!

Draw a **girl** in this box.

Draw a **tree** in this box.

Now circle the letter beside the answer that best describes your **girl doodle.**

1. My girl has eyes.

a. no **b.** yes

2. My girl has a mouth.

a. no **b.** yes

3. My girl has hands.

a. no **b.** yes

4. My girl has feet.

a. no **b.** yes

5. The lines in my drawing most closely match . . .

a. this light stroke. **b.** this medium stroke. **c.** this heavy stroke.

6. My girl takes up . . .

a. less than half the box. **b.** exactly half the box. **c.** more than half the box.

Scoring

Give yourself **1 point** for every **a** answer, **2 points** for every **b** answer, and **3 points** for every **c** answer. Then add them up to get your **girl score.**

1. ________
2. +________
3. +________
4. +________
5. +________
6. +________

=___11___ **girl score**

Now circle the letter beside the answer that best describes your **tree doodle.**

1. My tree has leaves.

a. no　　**b.** yes

2. My tree has branches.

a. no　　**b.** yes

3. My tree has a trunk that's an inch or wider.

a. no　　**b.** yes

4. My tree has grass growing around it.

a. no　　**b.** yes

5. The lines in my drawing most closely match . . .

a. this light stroke.　　**b.** this medium stroke.　　**c.** this heavy stroke.

6. My tree takes up . . .

a. less than half the box.　　**b.** exactly half the box.　　**c.** more than half the box.

Scoring

Give yourself **1 point** for every **a** answer, **2 points** for every **b** answer, and **3 points** for every **c** answer. Then add them up to get your **tree score.**

1. ________

2. +________

3. +________

4. +________

5. +________

6. +________

=__11__ **tree score**

Now add your **girl score** and **tree score** together, then find out how you doodle.

_______ **girl score**
+_______ **tree score**
=___22___ **total doodle score**

24 to 28 doodle score
Daring Designer
You're not afraid to make your mark. You create with ease, feeling confident that whatever you do will turn out fine.

16 to 23 doodle score
Careful Creator
You like to think things through before you start. You are growing bolder as time goes by—which gets a whole lot easier the more you try!

12 to 15 doodle score
Shy Sketcher
You may hesitate to make your mark. In groups, you probably prefer to blend in or be invisible, too. But everyone has something special to offer—including you! Why not let your colors show a little more?

Tidy Test

Are you **pretty neat** or **mostly messy?** Circle the letter next to the answer that describes you best.

1. When you get dressed for school in the morning, you . . .

a. put on the outfit you laid out last night.

b. look around in the closet for a while until you find your favorite shirt.

c. rummage through the laundry basket for something clean to wear.

2. When you want to put your hair up in a ponytail, you can find your favorite scrunchie . . .

a. stretched around the handle of your hairbrush where you always keep it.

b. on your dresser with all your other hair thingies.

c. under your bed with dust bunnies the size of Ping-Pong balls.

3. At the bottom of your backpack, you're most likely to find . . .

a. a pencil case.

b. an extra pair of gloves, pens, and a note from a friend.

c. empty candy wrappers, old tissues, and the lunch money you thought you lost the other day.

4. Your school locker is . . .

a. neat as a pin.

b. a little cluttered.

c. a disaster area.

5. During English class, you hand in a book report. Your paper looks . . .

a. perfect.

b. a little smudged but readable.

c. like your dog really did eat it.

6. You get caught in a thunderstorm on your way home from school. When you walk in the door cold and wet, you . . .

a. take off your boots and put them on a mat by the door to dry.

b. kick off your boots as you run to the bathroom to get some tissues.

c. head to the kitchen to make hot chocolate, leaving a trail of puddles along the way.

7. You eat a bowl of ice cream while doing homework in your room. When you're finished, you . . .

(a.) **wash and dry the bowl and spoon, then put them away.**

b. **rinse the bowl and spoon, then leave them in the kitchen sink.**

c. **set the bowl and spoon on your nightstand. You'll take them to the kitchen in the morning.**

8. When it's time to hit the sack, your bed is . . .

(a.) **neatly made.**

b. **tousled but tidy.**

c. **hidden by clothes and magazines.**

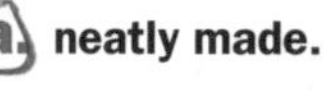

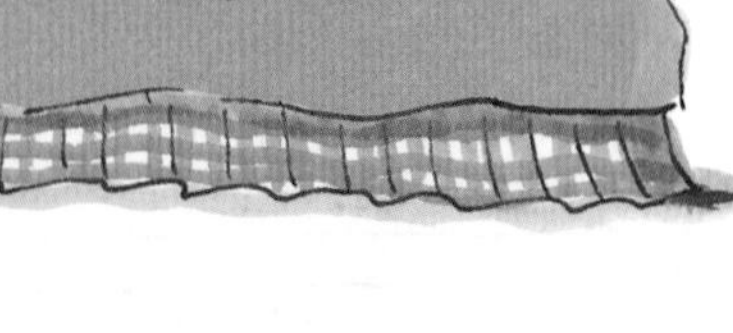

Answers

Mostly a's
Pretty Neat

You tidy up and organize wherever you go. Keeping things clean and orderly helps you focus on more important stuff throughout the day.

Mostly b's
Kinda Comfy

You're comfortable with a little clutter. Your room just wouldn't feel like a place you could relax or play in if *everything* were organized and tucked away. Besides, you can probably find the important things when you need them.

Mostly c's
Mostly Messy

No doubt about it—you're messy. Wouldn't it be nice to find things when you need them? You may want to try setting aside a little time each week to put your things in order.

Are You Too Nice?

Are you a **marshmallow softie** or a **smart cookie?** Circle the letter next to the answer that describes you best.

1. You've been waiting in line at the snack counter forever. When it's finally your turn, another girl butts in line ahead of you. You . . .

a. try to remember that who goes first really doesn't matter in the big picture of things and wait patiently to place your order next.

b. glare at her so that she knows just how disgusted you are with her piggy behavior.

c. say, "Excuse me, but I believe it was my turn next." Then place your order.

2. Your social studies group has been assigned a project for class, but you're the only one doing any work. You . . .

a. do all the work. You don't want to let the group down.

b. grumble a lot while doing the work and hope the others get the hint.

c. explain that it's not fair to have you do all the work and ask the others to pitch in.

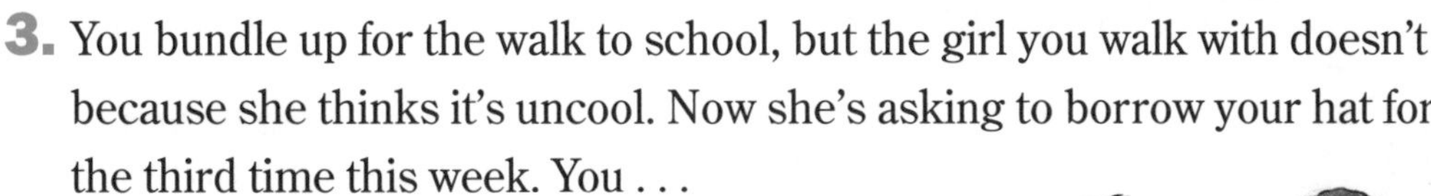

3. You bundle up for the walk to school, but the girl you walk with doesn't because she thinks it's uncool. Now she's asking to borrow your hat for the third time this week. You . . .

a. hand it over. How can you let her shiver?

b. tell her no at first but then give in when she starts to cough and sniffle.

c. say you'd rather not because you hate it when your head gets cold.

4. "You look adorable. Let's buy it!" squeals Mom while adjusting the collar on the polka-dot dress you're trying on. You . . .

- **a.** say "O.K." and promise yourself that you'll only wear the dress to Grandma's house. That way none of your friends will see you in it.
- **b.** shrug your shoulders and let Mom buy it. You'll hang it in your closet and hope she forgets about it.
- **c.** say, "I'll never wear it. Can we find something else that we both like?"

5. A friend keeps blowing off your plans at the last minute. You . . .

- **a.** understand and forgive her. She always has a good reason.
- **b.** know you should tell her how disappointed you are, but you don't. You don't want her to get mad.
- **c.** tell her how you feel and how you want to be treated. Then give her a chance to change her ways.

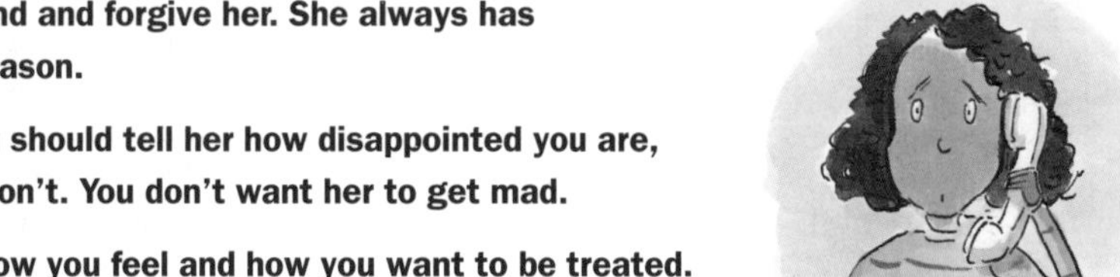

6. You're at the mall with your best friend when you both spot a fabulous T-shirt at the same time. You . . .

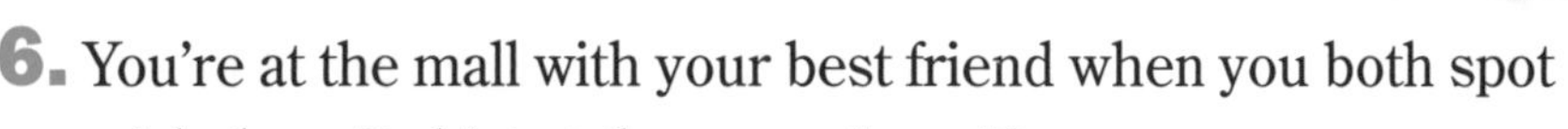

- **a.** let her buy it. That's what a good friend does, right?
- **b.** tell your friend you don't think it's a good color for her and hope that she'll lose interest so you can buy it.
- **c.** suggest that you each buy one in a different color.

7. You're sure you ordered fries with your cheeseburger, but you get a baked potato instead. You . . .

- **a.** say nothing. A baked potato is healthier anyway.
- **b.** ask your dad if he'll swap his fries for your potato.
- **c.** tell the waitress that there's been a mistake.

8. You invite two friends over to play a new board game, but while you're reading the instructions, they decide they'd rather go Rollerblading. You . . .

a. go along with them despite feeling disappointed. You don't want to force them to do something they don't want to do.

b. come up with reasons why their plan won't work: there's too much traffic, your skating socks aren't clean, and it looks like it's going to rain.

c. tell them how disappointed you feel and talk them into giving the game a chance.

Answers

Mostly a's
Marshmallow Softie

You may be too soft and sweet for your own good. You get stuck doing things you don't like to do and give up what you want just to please others or to keep the peace. Next time you start to soften, ask yourself what it is that *you* really want or think. Then speak up and see what happens. You'll feel stronger having done so.

Mostly b's
Candy-Coated Peanut

You may be sweet on the outside but going nuts underneath. You know what you want and how you really feel about things. The problem is you don't say it. Don't expect people to read your mind—speak up! Saying what you want may be hard at first, but it will get easier with practice.

Mostly c's
Chocolate-Chip Cookie

You're a smart cookie who is chock-full of sweetness! You understand that it's important to speak up for yourself in a semisweet way and let the chips fall where they may. People are likely to respect your honesty and confidence.

Good Cents

Imagine you just received **$50** for your birthday. How would you **spend** it? Answer the questions and **keep track** of what you make or spend.

1. At the bookstore, you find two new titles from your favorite mystery series. You . . .

a. buy one now and wait until you finish it before buying the other. **$3.50**

b. buy both of them. Who knows if you'll find these titles again? **$7.00**

c. wait and borrow them from the library. **$0**

$ 0

2. For lunch at the pool, you . . .

a. get a cheeseburger, fries, and a soda at the snack shop. **$3.00**

b. eat the lunch you packed. **$0**

c. order in a pizza with the works for you and your friends. **$10.00**

$ 0

3. Hot dogs are two for $1.00 at the ballpark today. You . . .

a. buy two, even though just one will fill you up. **$1.00**

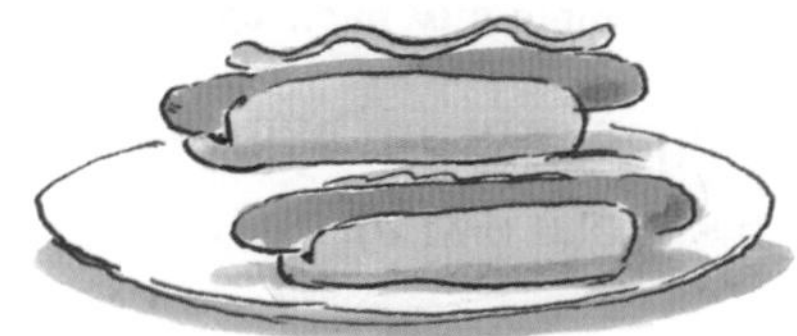

b. buy a bag of chips to hold you over till dinner. **25¢**

c. buy one. **50¢**

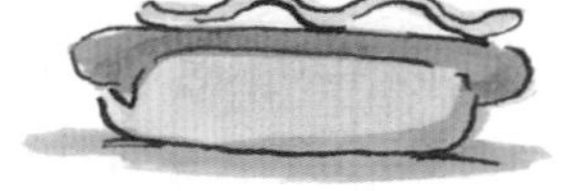

$ 50

4. At the school carnival, you spot a cute stuffed gorilla prize. You . . .

a. throw darts until the gorilla is yours!

$10.00

b. pass it by, knowing you could buy one for less than it would take to win it.

$0

c. throw a few darts but give up after three tries.

$3.00

$ 0

5. Your neighbor is having a garage sale. You . . .

a. buy a faded pair of jeans to cut into shorts for summer.

$2.00

b. buy a ton of stuff, even if you don't really need it. Everything's so cheap!

$5.00

c. set up a lemonade stand for thirsty sale-goers.

Make $8.00!

$ 8.00

6. When you hear the ice cream truck coming down the street, you . . .

a. run outside and buy a supersize rocket pop with bubble gum inside.

$1.00

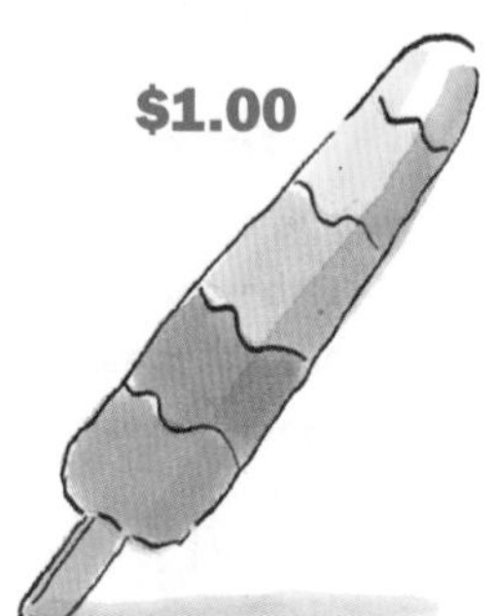

b. wander over and buy a Popsicle to split with your brother.

50¢

c. go to the freezer and pop out the orange juice cubes you froze earlier.

$0

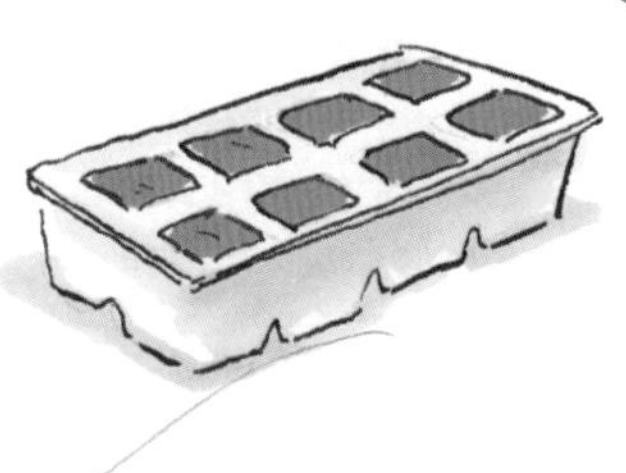

$ 50

7. A friend invited you to her birthday slumber party. You go shopping for a gift and buy . . .

a. a poster of Rocky Rockburn, everyone's favorite rock star—last year. It's on sale.

$2.00

b. a scrapbook for the birthday girl to put all her party photos in.

$8.00

c. earrings for your friend and PJ's for yourself. You want to have the best PJ's at the party.

$15.00

$ 2.00

Answers

Subtract or add what you spent or made from **$50.**

	$50.00	**Birthday Money**
–	4.00	**Money Spent**
+	8.00	**Money Earned**
=	$54.00	**Total Left**

$10 or Less Left

Hole in Your Pocket?

Money probably slips easily through your fingers. Before your funds dry up, think before you buy. Do you really need that stuffed gorilla? Try saving some money or even making a little of your own.

$11 to $34 Left

Money Minder

You're a smart spender and a savvy saver. You like to treat yourself every now and then, but you also know not to give in to spur-of-the-moment spending.

$35 or More Left

Smart Saver

You'd rather save money than spend it. Even when you do spend money, you're usually very resourceful about it. Your good cents may add up to a fortune-filled future!

Silly Scale

Are you **hungry** for **humor?** Weigh in on the silly scale to find out. Circle the letter next to the answer that fits you best.

1. People are more likely to tell you . . .

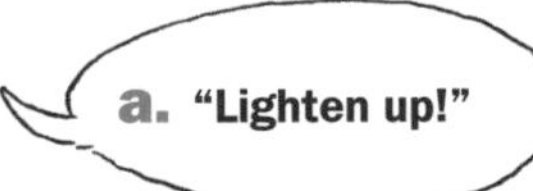

2. When you're with a group of classmates or friends, you tend to . . .

a. make sure things go according to plan.

b. play the clown.

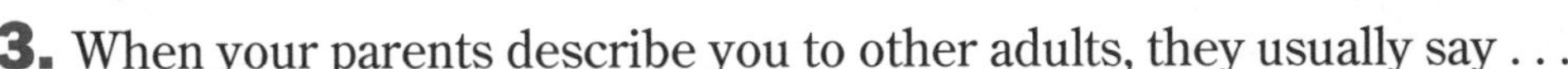

3. When your parents describe you to other adults, they usually say . . .

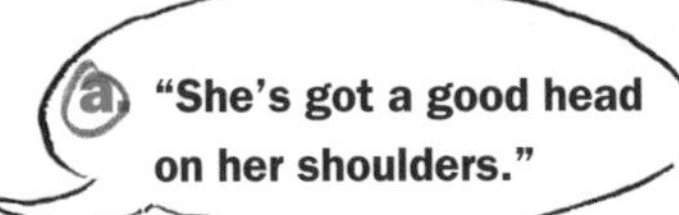

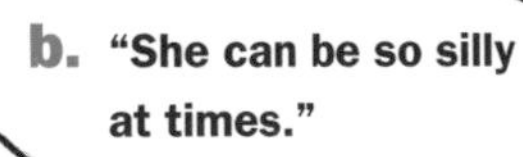

4. If you could choose where to go on your next class field trip, you would choose . . .

5. When someone makes a joke in class, you usually . . .

a. giggle and then get back to what you were doing.

b. laugh and shout out a joke of your own.

6. To you a great gift would be . . .

a. a book about cats.

b. a book of knock-knock jokes.

7. If your name was Nicole, you'd prefer to be called . . .

a. Nicole

b.

8. The first part of the Sunday newspaper you read is . . .

a. the front page.

b. the comics.

9. When you get to pick what to watch on TV, you choose . . .

a. soap operas.

b. cartoons.

Answers

0 to 3 b's = Silly **4 or 5 b's = Sillier** **6 to 9 b's = Silliest**

Do You Dare?

Are you **bold** and **brave** or do you **look** before you **leap?**
Circle the letter next to the answer that describes you best.

1. You've never had sushi before. So when you go out to eat at a Japanese restaurant for Mom's birthday, you . . .

a. **order the shrimp since you know what that's like.**

b. **go for the raw eel sashimi with fish eggs on top. You can't knock it until you try it, right?**

c. **ask the waiter, "Are you sure you don't have any hamburgers?"**

2. You've always dreamed about being onstage. When you see a poster for a school musical, you decide to . . .

a. **audition for the chorus. If you mess up, the others will cover for you.**

b. **try out for the lead part. Someone has to get it. It might as well be you!**

c. **volunteer for the stage crew. Although you'd love to be the star, it's just too scary.**

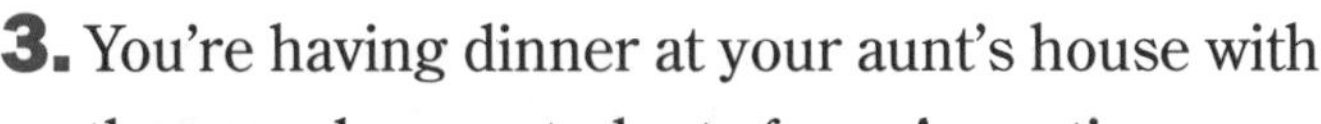

3. You're having dinner at your aunt's house with three exchange students from Argentina. Everyone is speaking Spanish. You . . .

a. **smile a lot but keep quiet and motion for the butter when you need it.**

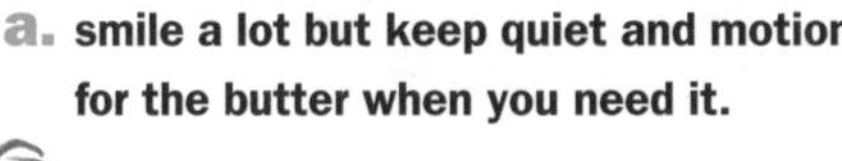

b. **say all the Spanish words you know and learn new ones, too!**

c. **hang out with your uncle in the kitchen, where things aren't so confusing.**

4. You go boating with a friend and her family. After you watch everyone else water-ski, they ask if you'd like to try. You . . .

a. ask a lot of questions first.

b. dive right in.

c. change the subject by asking, "When's lunch?"

5. You make a pact with a friend to paint your faces for the big Bobcats game. You . . .

a. paint two small stripes on your cheek. You don't want to look too goofy.

b. paint a stripe down your nose, "Go Cats" on one cheek, and a paw print on the other.

c. chicken out and avoid your friend at the game.

6. You're at the airport picking up Grandma when you spy your favorite rock star on the moving walkway. You . . .

a. follow her until she disappears into a "members only" lounge.

b. rush up to her and start chatting, then ask for an autograph.

c. try not to stare.

Answers

Mostly a's
Look, Then Leap

You dare with care. You like to ask questions and think about the risks before taking the plunge and having fun.

Mostly b's
Bold and Brave

You don't think twice about doing a new and different thing. You figure you won't know if you like it until you try it.

Mostly c's
Safe, Not Sorry

You go with what you know and do what feels comfortable. Just remember that doing or learning something new can be fun, too!

Pal Poll

Answer these questions with a **friend** in mind, then ask her to check your answers.

1. The three things my friend likes best about herself are activeness, smartness, and funnyness.

2. Her most prized possession is her skis.

3. The best birthday present she could get is a tennis raquet.

4. Her pet peeve is a clownfish.

5. She would most likely doodle . . .

a. cute puppies, kitties, or stick people.

(b) flowers, trees, a sun, or a moon.

c. stars, arrows, hearts, or curlicues.

d. triangles, boxes, or other geometric shapes.

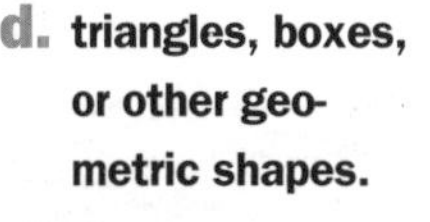

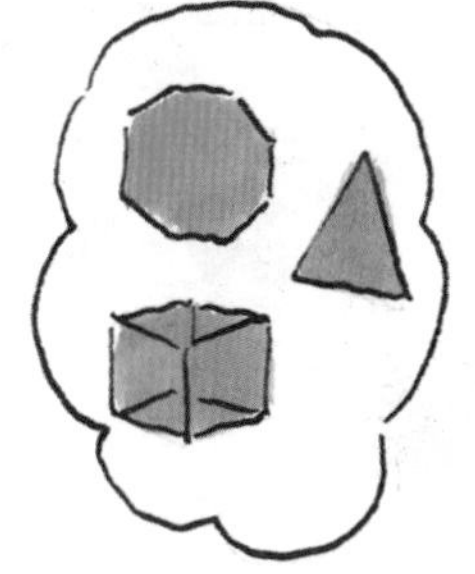

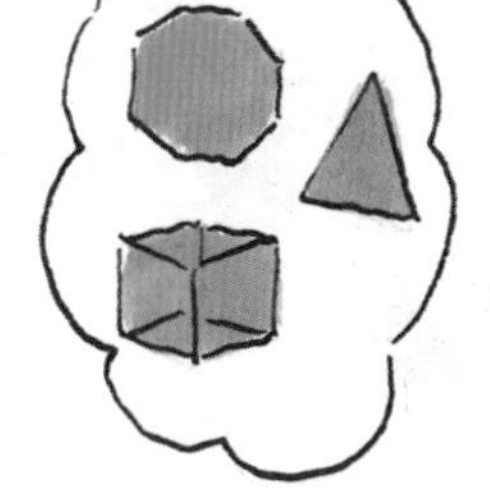

6. She would be least likely to do the following in front of other people . . .

a. sing a solo. **b.** dance. **c.** give an oral report. **d.** act in a play.

7. Her favorite flavor of ice cream is chocolate.

8. Her favorite color of jelly bean is green.

9. When it comes to snacking, she has . . .

a. a sweet tooth. **b.** salt attacks. **c.** healthy habits. **d.** a spicy streak.

10. Her favorite music group or singer is Green Day.

11. The movie that she would rent again and again is Harry Potter.

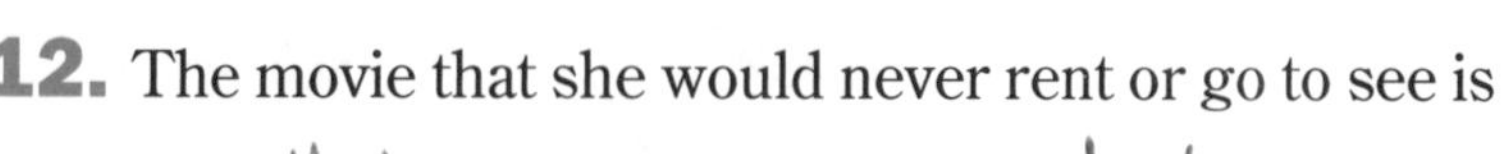

12. The movie that she would never rent or go to see is well he sees everything.

13. The one TV show she never misses is he's not allowed to watchTV.

14. She always says Tata let's play!.

15. Her favorite place to be alone is behind the couch.

16. She usually does her homework . . .

a. in front of the TV. **b.** in her room. **c.** at the kitchen table. **(d.)** with me!

17. Her favorite amusement park ride is Disney Land's Buzz Light Year.

18. Her favorite holiday is Holi.

19. Her dream vacation is Skiing on the glaciers or tennis in florida.

20. She would say that it's more important to be . . .

a. smart. **b.** pretty. **c.** wealthy. **d.** athletic.

Answers

Score **1 point** for each correct answer.

16 to 20 points

You must care a lot about your friend to know her as well as you do—inside out and through and through. If she knows you as well as you know her, you're a lucky pair!

10 to 15 points

You know your friend very well, but you still discover something new every now and then. That's all part of the fun of becoming even better friends.

0 to 9 points

There's always more to learn about a friend. You two probably have a lot of discoveries ahead of you. Explore and enjoy!

Pssst!

Can you **keep** a **secret?** Circle the answer that most closely describes what you'd do in each situation.

1. Your friend Chelsea told you what song she's singing at her audition for the musical and made you promise not to tell anyone. You . . .

- **(a.) keep it to yourself.**
- **b. tell only your best friend—she's not trying out for the musical anyway.**
- **c. tell everyone who's auditioning so they'll know how close you and Chelsea are.**

2. You and your friends have planned a surprise pizza party for Tracey tonight. So when Tracey orders pizza for lunch, you . . .

- **(a.) say nothing and hope she likes pizza a whole lot!**
- **b. say, "But that's what . . . you had yesterday," catching yourself midsentence.**
- **c. blurt out, "But we're having pizza tonight. Oops!"**

3. When no one is looking, Grandma slips you $10. "Here's a little reward for your good grades. It'll be our secret," she whispers. You . . .

- **(a.) smile and quickly stuff the money in your pocket.**
- **b. are so excited, you have to tell Dad immediately. Too bad your brother overhears you.**
- **c. wave the $10 bill in your brother's face as soon as you leave Grandma's house.**

4. You overhear your math teacher say he's getting engaged over break. When you congratulate him later, he asks you to keep it a secret so the class doesn't get distracted. You . . .

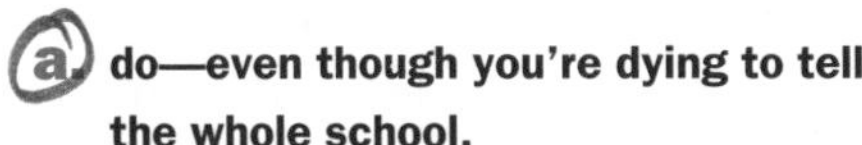

a. do—even though you're dying to tell the whole school.

b. tell a few friends but don't name any names.

c. squeal, squeal, squeal! News this big is too exciting not to reveal!

5. You see your friend Melissa at the store buying a training bra. Melissa gets really embarrassed and asks you not to tell anyone. You . . .

a. keep her secret. You wouldn't want anyone blabbing the news when your day comes.

b. tell only your best friend. She just got a bra, too, and will understand.

c. talk about how many girls in class have bras at recess the next day. You include Melissa in the list.

6. You see your brother out riding his bike—but he's supposed to be grounded! He begs you to keep quiet about it. You . . .

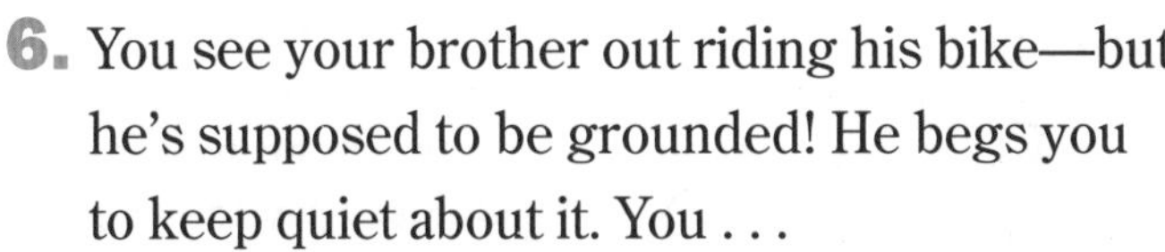

a. pretend you never saw him.

b. wave and give him a big, cheesy smile. Now he has to let you use the computer whenever you want—or else!

c. rush home and tell Mom. It's payback time.

Answers

Mostly a's
Lips Are Sealed

Secrets are safe with you! Once your lips are sealed, you throw away the key. Bravo! You have a good understanding of privacy and know the value of keeping your word. You probably don't even reveal the things you've accidentally seen or overheard.

Mostly b's
Sometimes Slip

You know when you shouldn't be letting a secret out, but sometimes it just slips. And other times you can't resist the excitement of being the one to share great gossip. But you know that you can do better at keeping your lips sealed. Listen to your conscience and think before you speak. Others will be glad you did!

Mostly c's
Loose Lips

Your loose lips let everything slip. When you break your word about keeping a secret, you show people that they can't count on you to be trustworthy. Unless you're willing to let your friendships suffer and get a reputation as a big blabbermouth, it's time to take your promises more seriously and keep those secrets to yourself. Zip those lips!

Are You a Class Act?

What's your **school style?** Circle the letter next to the answer that describes you best.

1. When the class bell rings, you're . . .

a. at your desk with your pencil sharpened and notebook open.

b. rooting around in your desk for your lucky purple pencil.

c. hanging out at the pencil sharpener, waving to the cars that drive by outside.

2. When you glance at your weekly planner, you find . . .

a. test dates and assignments listed.

b. dozens of doodles.

c. Who needs a planner when you can call your friends?

3. Before the weekly vocabulary test, you . . .

a. quiz yourself with flash cards each night.

b. read the definitions over and over again while eating breakfast the morning of the test.

c. ask to go see the school nurse as soon as your teacher starts handing out the test.

4. While studying fossils in science class, you . . .

a. take notes about all the neat rocks.

b. use the magnifying glass to examine your hair cuticles.

c. daydream about dinosaurs.

5. Class elections are coming up. You . . .

a. run for president!

b. vote for the girl who is having a slumber party next weekend.

c. draw mustaches on the campaign posters hanging in the hall.

6. Your English teacher drops a hint that there might be a pop quiz on Friday. You . . .

a. make a note in your planner.

b. make a mental note to remember to study.

c. sigh and roll your eyes.

7. You're in social studies class, dying to talk with your best friend. You . . .

a. plan to catch her right after class.

b. try to listen to what the teacher is saying as you dash off a short note to her.

c. tune out the teacher and write your friend a two-page note, pass it along, and watch her read it.

8. When your teacher asks a question in class, you usually . . .

a. raise your hand to answer.

b. wait to be called upon, even though you think you know the answer.

c. hide behind your book.

9. When your class goes to the library, you . . .

a. find a book for your next report.

b. whisper, giggle, and get "shushed" by the librarian.

c. curl up on the reading chair with a Gameboy.

10. A friend invites you to her house after school, but a book report is due tomorrow. You . . .

a. tell your friend you'll come another day.

b. go for a little while and plan to stay up late to finish the book.

c. go and have a great time, then ask your sister to tell you what the book is about.

Answers

Mostly a's

Class Act

You're putting all you've got into your schoolwork. And you're a lucky girl because you know that the more you put into what you do, the more you get out of it.

Mostly b's

Class Passer

Sometimes you try, but other times you do just enough to get by. You're probably giving school only half your effort—and you're probably getting only half back.

Mostly c's

Class Slacker

Your body may be present at school, but your mind is most likely to be absent. If you pay more attention and put your heart into your work, you may find that it feels good to be part of the class.

Moment of Truth

How **honest** are you? Circle the letter next to the answer that most closely describes what you'd do in each situation.

1. You knew all the words for the Spanish test—or at least you thought you did. But now that you're taking the test, there's one word you can't recall. You . . .

- **a.** **whisper to the girl next to you and ask for the answer.**
- **b.** **try to spot the word on another girl's test.**
- **c.** **guess as well as you can and hope you can make up for any wrong answers with extra credit points.**

2. Your mom buys a box of fancy candies to serve at a party this weekend. "Keep out!" she warns. You sneak two right away. Then two more. Before you know it, you've eaten half the box. You . . .

- **a.** **wait to see what happens. Your little brother usually gets blamed for these sorts of things.**
- **b.** **decide to secretly replace the box and hope your mom won't notice.**
- **c.** **tell your mom and offer to pay for a new box out of your allowance.**

3. You're playing cards with a friend at the beach when you realize you can see all her cards reflected in her sunglasses. You . . .

- **a.** **win the game. Hooray!**
- **b.** **try not to look but peek when you're not sure which card to play.**
- **c.** **tell her about it and deal a new hand—one she plays with her sunglasses off.**

4. At lunch your friends ask about the poem you wrote for English class. "What poem?" you ask, suddenly remembering one was due today. You . . .

a. rush to the library, copy a poem out of a book, and put your name on it.

b. pretend to have a stomach ache and go to the school nurse to buy yourself time.

c. try to write something in a hurry. If you can't, explain to your teacher that you messed up and ask for an extension.

5. You accidentally hit a neighbor's window with a Frisbee. Your neighbor storms across the street and demands an apology just as your dad pulls up in the driveway and automatically jumps to your defense. You . . .

a. deny it. What's the big deal? You didn't break it.

b. say nothing but feel terrible and worry about what your dad would think if he knew the truth.

c. share the truth with Dad and apologize to your neighbor.

6. You're helping out at a local orchard and getting paid for each apple you pick. Your sister asks you if she can help out for fun. You . . .

a. let her help but don't tell her about the money you're making from her apples. She'll never know.

b. let her help, then use some of your earnings to treat her to ice cream.

c. tell her you're getting paid for the apples. Then you give her what she earns to put in her piggy bank.

7. When the movie is over at the multiplex cinema, you and your friend suddenly realize how easy it would be to sneak into another movie. You . . .

- **a.** think it's a great idea and follow your friend to the next theater.
- **b.** do it but worry the whole time about getting caught.
- **c.** regret missing the movie but don't sneak in because it's wrong.

8. You loan your sister a jacket. When you get it back, you find $10 in the pocket. You . . .

- **a.** consider it payment for the loan and go shopping!
- **b.** convince yourself it might have been yours. It was in a small pocket she might not have used or even noticed.
- **c.** ask your sister if it's hers.

Answers

If you answered a more than once . . .

Pants on Fire?

Be careful. One lie or dishonest act often leads to another. What's more, lies often hurt others and may ultimately hurt you. So what should you do? Tell the truth!

Mostly b's

Stretching the Truth

You tend to let the truth go unsaid when hiding it will benefit you. The thing is, you know you're being dishonest, and that doesn't feel too good inside. You'll feel better once you start being completely honest with yourself and others.

Mostly c's

Nothing but the Truth

You know what's right, and you usually do it. Even when you mess up, you're willing to fess up and take responsibility for your actions. Bravo! Stay true to yourself and keep your conscience free.

Friendship Rings

Get together with a **friend** and discover your **likes** and **dislikes.**

1. On a piece of paper, **write** down your **top ten things** in one of the categories at the right. Have your friend do the same, but don't talk about them until you're finished.

2. **Compare** your lists and **circle** any items you both listed. Then **write** these items in the **middle** of one of the sets of rings on the following pages.

3. **Write** the other items on your list to the side in one ring, and have your friend **list** the rest of her items in the other ring.

Friendship Ring Categories

- Cartoon Characters
- Wild Animals
- Snacks
- Sounds
- Board Games
- Books
- Road Trips
- TV Shows
- Pet Peeves
- Amusement Park Rides
- Sports to Play

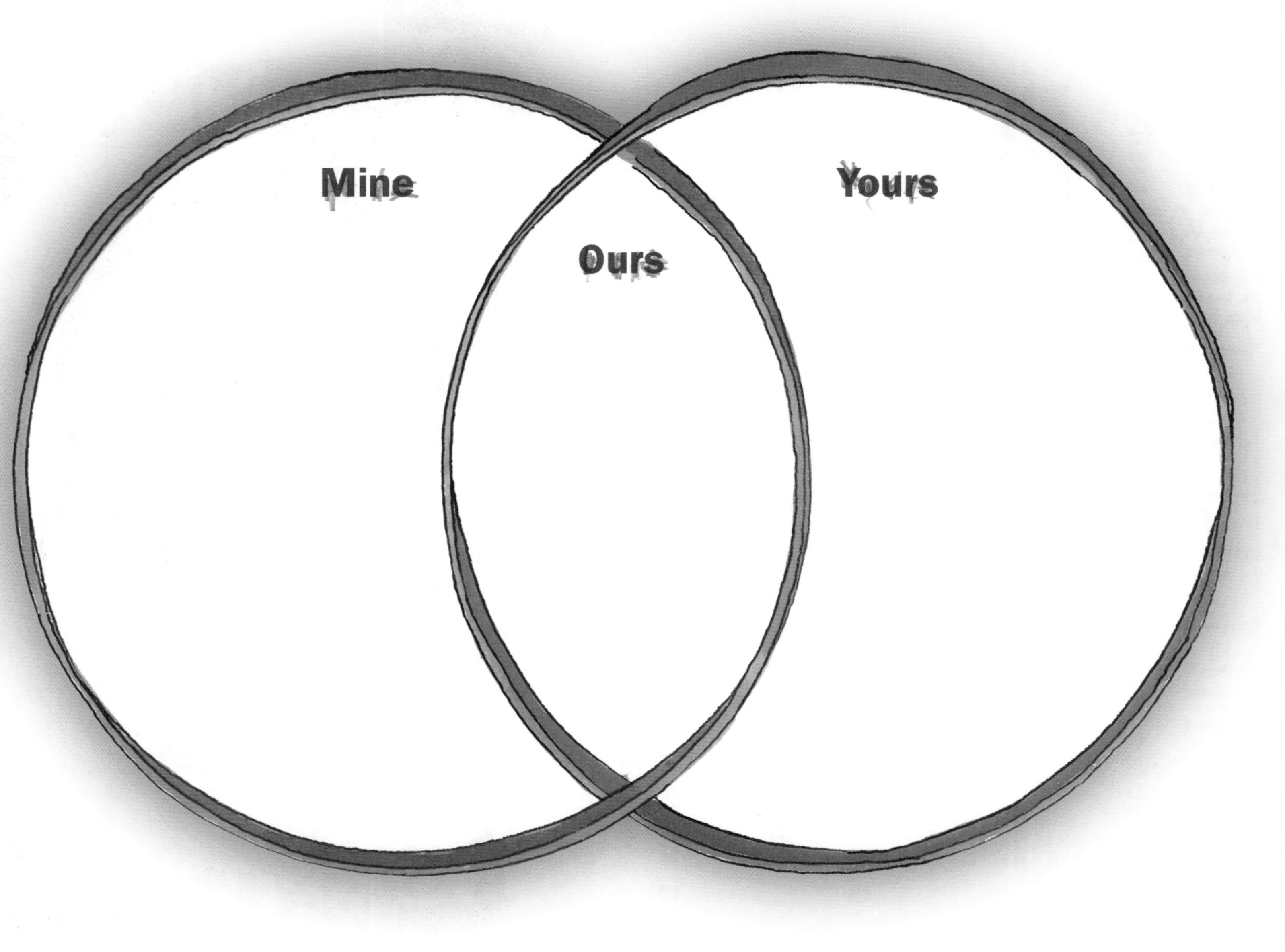
Mine
Ours
Yours

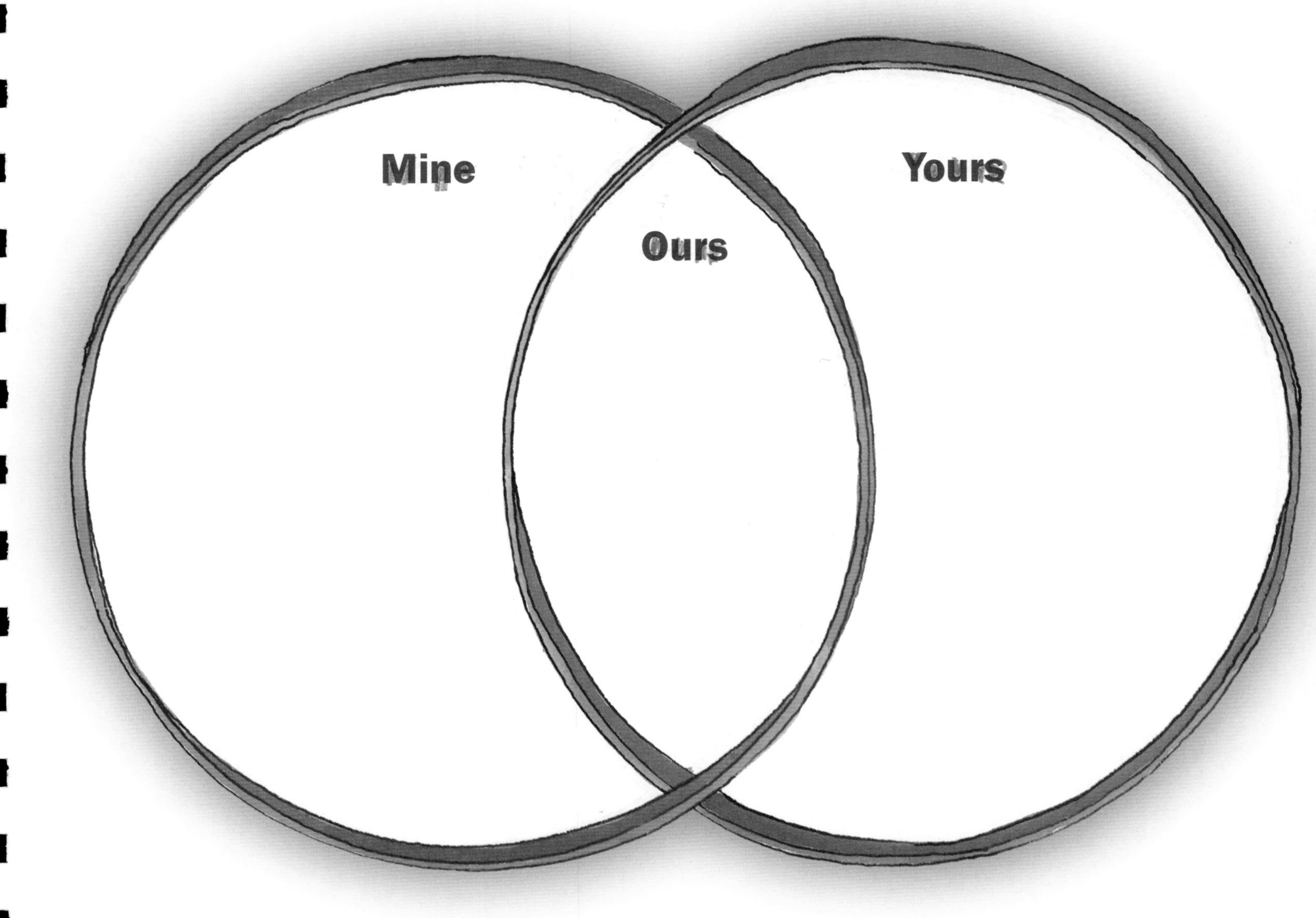
Mine
Ours
Yours

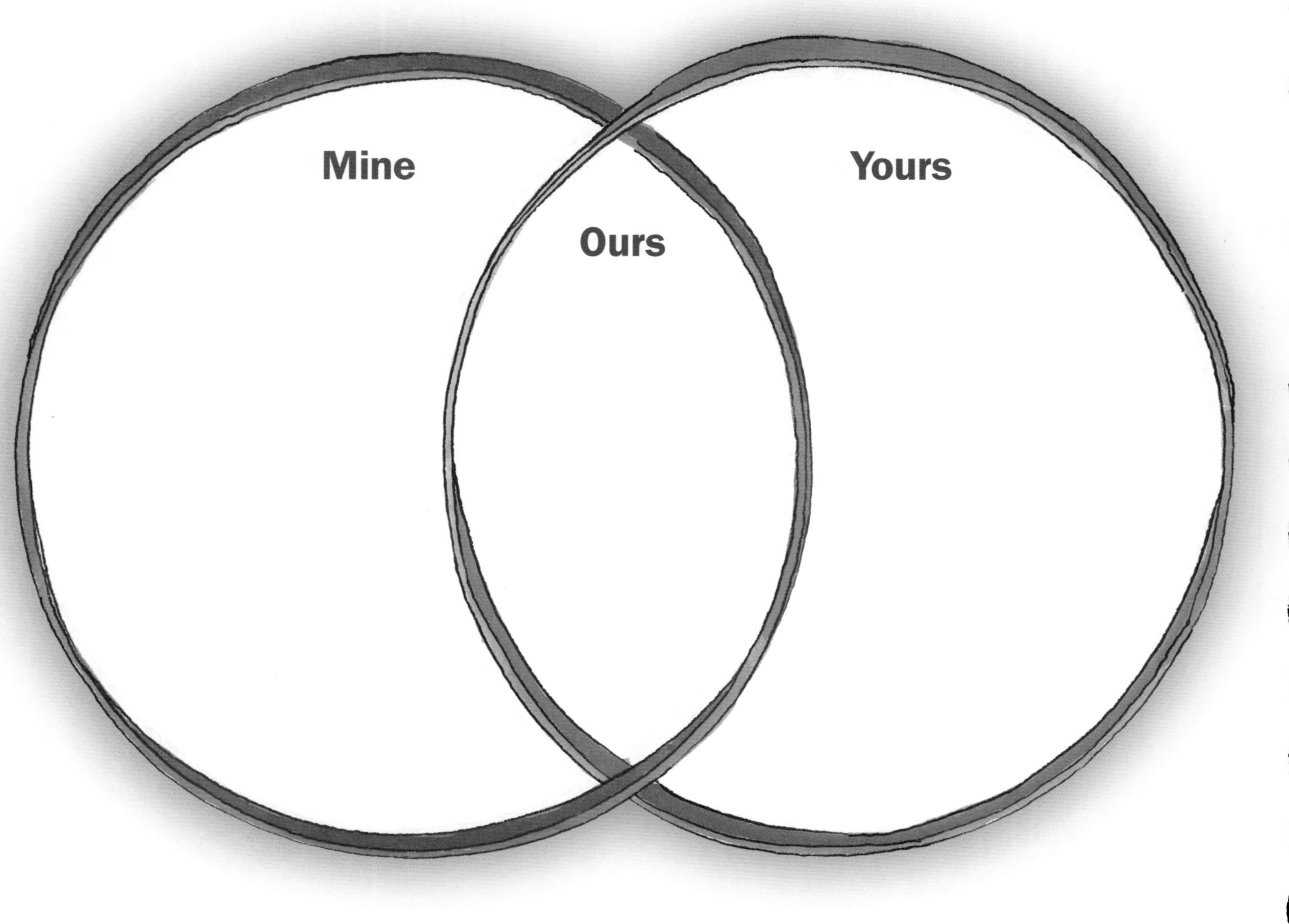
Mine
Ours
Yours

Reading Your Rings

One circle represents you, and the other represents your friend. The place where they **overlap** is where your likes or interests **blend.** The more things you have in the **middle** of the circles, the more **alike** you and your friend are. See how many favorites you **share.** Then pick another category and fill in more rings. If you run out of rings or categories, make up your own!

If you share . . .

5 or More Favorites

You're two peas in a pod. You have a lot in common and like to do many of the same things.

3 to 4 Favorites

You share many likes, but you also do different things from time to time.

1 to 2 Favorites

Did you learn something new about your likes and dislikes? Just because you don't have much in common in this area doesn't mean you don't have grounds for a great friendship. Choose another category and keep searching for what you both like.

What If Your Likes Just Never Overlap?

Opposites also attract! You two have fun sharing and exploring your likes and interests.

Losing Your Cool

What do you do when you **lose** your **cool?**
Circle the letter next to the answer that most closely describes what you'd do in each situation.

1. When you ask your friend Zoe to go swimming, she says she doesn't want to go to the pool today. So you go alone. But when you get there, you see Zoe hanging out—with another girl! You . . .

a. **say, "Hey! Some friend you are!"**

b. **make a quick exit so no one will see you cry.**

c. **leave before they spot you, and never mention the incident.**

d. **forget Zoe and look for other friends.**

2. During a big soccer game, you pass the ball to Nina. But the other team steals it from her and makes the winning goal. You . . .

a. **yell at Nina, "You blew it!"**

b. **feel like crying.**

c. **act like this is no big deal, even though you're a little disappointed.**

d. **tell your teammates never to pass the ball to Nina again.**

3. You're working on a project with your friend Amy. You write a good report, but Amy makes a sloppy poster to go along with it. Your team gets a low grade. You . . .

a. say, "I can't believe what a sloppy person you are! I'm never going to team up with you again."

b. get so upset you start to cry.

c. don't say anything because you don't want Amy to feel bad.

d. make sure everyone knows the low grade was Amy's fault.

4. Your dad promised to take you to the school carnival. But by the time he gets home, it's too late to go. You . . .

a. shout, "Thanks for nothing!" then stomp off and slam the door to your room.

b. watch TV as tears fill your eyes.

c. tell him it's O.K.—even though it's not.

d. give him the silent treatment for the whole week.

5. Your sister borrows your best shirt and returns it covered with stains. You . . .

a. yell, "What a pig! I'm never loaning you anything of mine again!"

b. try to wash out the stains as tears stream down your cheeks.

c. say nothing. Your parents will be furious if you start arguing.

d. take back the bracelet you gave her for her birthday.

6. You've made plans to go to the park with friends, but Mom says you have to stay home and help clean the house. You . . .

a. **scowl and shout, "I never get to have any fun!"**

b. **sniffle and sulk while folding the laundry.**

(c.) **take a deep breath and go get the furniture polish.**

d. **put darks and whites together in the same wash. Next time Mom won't want your help.**

Answers

Mostly a's

You tend to blurt hurtful words or act in loud, stormy ways when you're angry. Whether you do these things on purpose to get your point across or because you can't help it, consider this: yelling mean things or slamming doors doesn't really tell others why you're angry. So, you'd be better off saying, "I'm so mad, I need time to cool down!" Then take a few deep breaths, count to ten, or even go away for a while. You can come back and talk when you've recovered from being so mad.

Mostly b's

Crying is probably your way of getting your strong feelings out. In fact, it may be hard for you to put your angry feelings into words. It's O.K. to cry, but once you have, you may want to wash your face and then try to talk calmly about what made you so angry.

Mostly c's

You often cover up angry feelings because you don't want to hurt anyone or you figure that sharing how you feel won't make a difference anyway.

Actually, though, hiding your feelings can hurt you and your relationships, and it won't make things better. Tell people how you feel so that whatever bothered you in the first place is less likely to happen again.

Mostly d's

You have a tendency to want to "get even" with whoever has made you angry or to "make her see how she made you feel." Getting even or inflicting a similar hurt may seem fair, but it usually just makes things worse. If you really want to make things better, talk to the person with whom you're angry.

Can You Read Minds?

Body language can sometimes give you clues about what others are **thinking** or **feeling.**

Write the **letter** of each classmate next to what he or she **appears** to be **thinking.**

c **1.** **"Is it my turn yet? I'm so nervous."**

f **2.** **"Whatever."**

d **3.** **"Wow! That's cool."**

b **4.** **"I'm grumpy. When's lunch?"**

a **5.** **"I can't wait to go to the slumber party tonight."**

e **6.** **"Huh? I don't get it."**

Answers

1. c; 2. f; 3. d; 4. b; 5. a; 6. e

The Write Clues

Does your **handwriting** hold clues about you? **Write** and **see.**

Write a paragraph in the box below about anything at all. Don't try to make your handwriting come out a certain way. Just think about what you want to say so that you write naturally.

I'm eating something called kheer. It's very good. It's rice with sugar and yogurt. My brother's also eating kheer. My Grandma keep's telling to just eat and put this book down.

Now circle the letter next to the answer that best describes your handwriting.

1. How do your letters slant?

a. to the left
slant

b. to the right
slant

c. not much at all

What it might mean:

a. You're quiet, calm, and focused.

b. You plunge ahead with courage, enthusiasm, and a sense of adventure.

c. You're practical and reliable. You're often the one who gets the job done.

2. How hard do you press when you write?

a. not very hard

b. hard

girl

c. medium (circled)

girl

What it might mean:

a. You're gentle, sensitive, and a little shy. Sometimes you want to hide like invisibie ink.

b. You're energetic, forceful, and bold—unafraid to make your mark or speak your mind.

c. You don't get pushy or get pushed around. Instead, you strike a happy medium between bossy and laid-back.

3. How wide are your letters? Draw a box around an "n" to find out.

a. (circled) Is the box a perfect square?

rainbow

b. Is it wider than it is tall?

rainbow

c. Is it taller than it is wide?

rainbow

What it might mean:

a. You strike a balance between work and play.

b. You're friendly and chatty.

c. You like to focus on your goals before having a good time.

4. How do you cross your lowercase t's?

a. straight across **b.** slanting up **c.** slanting down

t t t

What it might mean:

a. You're approaching tasks with confidence and care.

b. You're aiming high and feeling ambitious.

c. You're getting down to work and going after what you want—and with your determination and persistence, you may just get it, too.

5. Where do you dot your lowercase i's?

a. a little to the right of the i **b.** a little to the left of the i **c.** exactly above the i

i i i

What it might mean:

a. You make decisions quickly. You like to work fast and not worry about the details.

b. You tend to put things off until later.

c. You crave perfection and try to be precise in all you do.

6. What do the lower loops on your letters look like?

a. long and full

b. big and round

c. long or hooked but not fully looped

d. so short and thin that they're not really there

loopy

What it might mean:

a. Whether you're running for class president or trying out for band soloist, you want to be the center of attention.

b. From playing sports to baking cookies, you like to keep busy.

c. When it comes to math equations, mystery novels, even jigsaw puzzles, you won't quit until you find a solution.

d. You're a practical-minded girl who likes to find the fastest way to do something. You take the shortcut home from school and pop popcorn in the microwave.

7. Now look at the lines you wrote. Do they go . . .

a. uphill

We went to the beach.

b. downhill

We went to the beach.

c. up and down like waves

We went to the beach.

What it might mean:

a. You're feeling happy.

b. You're feeling blue.

c. Your feelings may be just like the lines of your handwriting: up one minute and down the next.

Parent Poll

How well do you know **Mom** or **Dad?** Take this quiz with a parent in mind, then ask him or her to check your answers.

1. Middle name Rose

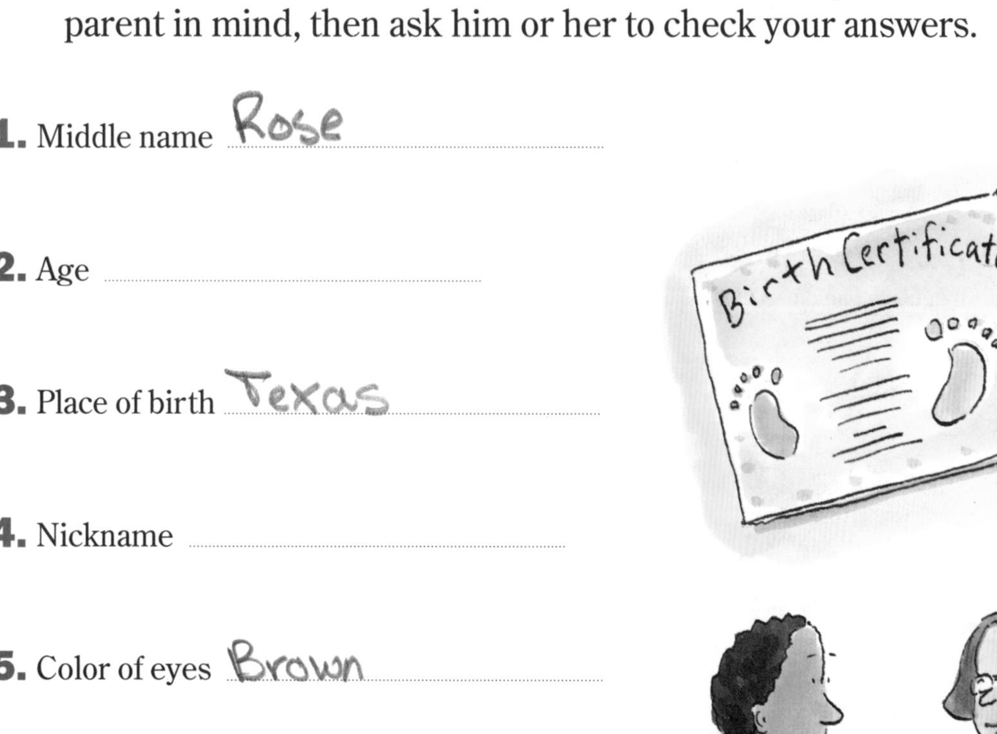

2. Age

3. Place of birth Texas

4. Nickname

5. Color of eyes Brown

6. Right- or left-handed right

7. Best friend

8. Favorite relative

9. Official title at work Dr. Orendain

10. Dream job OBGYN

11. Most admired person ....

12. Favorite author ....

13. Least favorite chore ....

14. Favorite recipe to make ....

15. Favorite restaurant ....

16. Favorite family vacation spot ....

17. Front, back, or middle of roller coaster

....

18. Favorite sport ....

19. Favorite day of the year ....

20. Favorite thing to do on Saturday afternoon ....

....

21. Least favorite word that you say

Yep or Yeah

22. Pet peeve (the one thing that really drives him or her crazy)

....

23. Favorite room in the house ....

24. The one thing he or she can't leave home without

....

25. Favorite music ....

26. Favorite radio station ....

27. Favorite movie star

28. Word or phrase said most often

29. Worst present ever received

30. Favorite pizza topping

Answers

Score **1 point** for each question you answered correctly.

20 to 30 points
Parent Pal
You're in tight with Mom or Dad. Knowing your parent so well shows how much you care.

10 to 19 points
Family Familiar
You're pretty familiar with Mom or Dad—and now you know even more!

0 to 9 points
Parent Dare
Dare to know your parent better. Take time to notice likes and dislikes, habits or hobbies. There's lots more to share.

Are You Ready for a Pet?

Should you go for the **golden retriever** or stick to **stuffed animals?** Take this quiz to find out.

1. It's your week to care for the class rabbit, and you notice you're running low on food. You . . .

a. write a note for the teacher to let her know.

b. guess that you have enough left for a couple more days. You can always feed the bunny carrots if you run out.

c. forget about it. The teacher will take care of it.

2. When you visit your friend, her puppy Poochie always barks and jumps on you, even though your friend doesn't want him to. You . . .

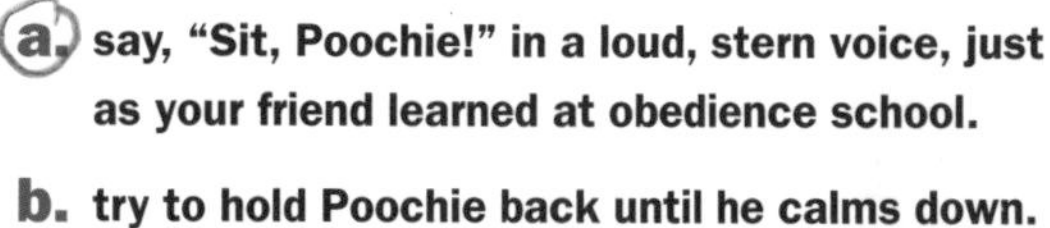

a. say, "Sit, Poochie!" in a loud, stern voice, just as your friend learned at obedience school.

b. try to hold Poochie back until he calms down.

c. clap your hands and encourage Poochie to jump and bark more. It's fun—even if he's misbehaving.

3. You're picking up your friend for a movie when she discovers that Poochie has had another accident on the kitchen floor. "Oh, no!" she says and runs for the paper towels. You . . .

a. volunteer to take Poochie outside for a couple of minutes while your friend cleans up the mess.

b. wait impatiently while your friend scrambles to wipe up the puddle and take Poochie for a quick walk.

c. tell her to leave the mess for her mom to clean up. You're in a hurry.

4. When Aunt Susan brings her cat Raku over to stay with your family while she's on vacation, you . . .

a. say hi to Raku and scratch her under the chin—her favorite spot. Then get the lowdown from your aunt about how to care for Raku.

b. chase Raku around the room and pick her up, even though she seems a little scared. You love cuddling cats!

c. ask your aunt, "Do I really have to clean her litter box *every* day?"

5. When Raku wakes you up early the next morning by nuzzling your face and purring very loudly, you . . .

a. cuddle for a minute, then get up and feed her.

b. throw a sock on the floor for her to play with, then pull the covers up over your head and try to go back to sleep.

c. put her out in the hall. Maybe someone else will get up and feed her.

6. When you go downstairs to get your soccer jersey from the laundry, you notice that Raku's cat litter box smells bad. You . . .

a. change the litter and take the smelly stuff out to the trash can.

b. scoop out the lumps for now. You'll change the litter after the game . . . if you remember.

c. spray air freshener around the litter box, then skip off to the soccer game.

Answers

Mostly a's

With your sense of commitment and responsibility, you have the potential to become a great pet owner. There's a lot to consider when you get a new critter. So read up and learn even more about your new pet before bringing it home.

Mostly b's

You may not be prepared to take care of a pet that needs a lot of attention or to train an animal to behave properly. Before you get a pet of your own, try taking care of someone else's pet first. Volunteer to walk and play with a neighbor's dog or to feed an animal that's kept in your science room at school. If you like the experience and stick with it for more than a week or two, put some more thought into getting a pet of your own.

Mostly c's

If you really want something cute to cuddle and name, you should probably stick with stuffed animals for now. Read up on pet care and training, and spend time with a friend's or neighbor's pet.

Food for Thought

Do your manners **shine** at **dinnertime,** or do they need **polish?** Take this quiz to find out.

1. The turkey's carved, and you get your plate first. It smells great, and you can hardly wait to dig in. You . . .

- **a. dig in! After all, you don't want the food to get cold.**
- **b. wait until everybody else has been served and the hostess takes a bite before you dig in.**
- **c. take little nibbles when you think nobody is looking.**

2. Oh, no! There's a UFO on your plate—an Unidentified Food Object. You . . .

- **a. say, "I'm not eating that."**
- **b. take a tiny taste to see if you like it.**
- **c. hide it under some turkey skin.**

3. Leave it to Aunt Beth to be fancy. There are three forks at your place. Three?! Which one should you use first?

- **a. Watch and see which one the hostess uses, and use the same one.**
- **b. Ask. There's no such thing as a dumb question, right?**
- **c. Start with the outside one first.**

4. You wanted to sit next to Cousin Wendy. Instead, you're sitting by Granny Smith. "Hello, sweet pea," she says. "How's school?" You . . .

a. say "Fine!" while looking around to see where Cousin Wendy is sitting.

b. pretend you didn't hear her and make an igloo out of your mashed potatoes.

c. tell Granny all about your art project. Then you ask her about her new glasses.

5. From the end of the table, your dad says, "Please pass the peas." They're sitting in front of you, so you . . .

a. pass the peas to the right.

b. pass the peas to the left.

c. scoop up some peas and say, "Please pass your plate, Dad."

6. Halfway through the meal, you notice that Aunt Shannon has a glob of cranberry stuck in her teeth. You . . .

a. catch her eye and make a little motion with your hand by your mouth to let her know.

b. say, "Hey, Shannon. You've got something stuck in your teeth!"

c. do nothing. You don't want to embarrass her!

7. Uncle Andrew is telling you a long story when you realize you really, really have to go to the bathroom. You . . .

a. say, "Was that a knock at the door?" and run from the table.

b. sit there until you think you're going to explode, because it's rude to interrupt.

c. say, "Excuse me, Uncle Andrew." Then ask the hostess, "May I be excused for a moment, please?"

Answers

1. The answer is **b.** It's not polite to eat in front of somebody who doesn't have any food. Why? Because watching you eat makes that person hungrier. The hostess is in charge of making sure everybody is served. Then she'll begin eating—and so can you.

2. The answer is **b.** If somebody puts something new on your plate, you should give it a try. Hiding it fools no one, and telling the cook you don't like the looks of it is just as rude.

3. The answers are **a, b,** and **c.** They're all right! Whenever you aren't sure what to do, ask someone or just wait and see what the hostess does. But there's also a nifty secret to every fancy place setting: the silverware for the food that's served first is placed farthest from the plate.

4. The answer is **c.** Conversation is the most important part of a meal, so don't clam up just because you aren't sitting next to your favorite relative. Be friendly! Ask some questions. You and Granny will never get to know each other if you don't give good conversation a chance.

5. The answer is **a.** Pass food, not plates. Food is passed to the right. If you send something the wrong way, two platters are going to end up nose to nose. If it's a big dish, help the next person by holding it while she serves herself.

6. The answer is **a.** If you tell the whole table that Aunt Shannon's got a glob in her teeth, she will be embarrassed. But letting her go through the whole meal with that glob will probably embarrass her more. The kindest thing is to let her know in a private way that she needs to clean her teeth.

7. The answer is **c.** There are times when it's O.K. to interrupt an adult if you do so nicely, and this is one of those times. Most adults will understand what you're thinking, and you can slip away without any fuss.

Starring You!

What do your **dreams** of **fame** and **fortune** say about you? To find out, draw a star around the letter of the answer you choose.

1. Which of these TV shows would you want to star in?

2. If someone were to write your life story, what would you want the title to be?

3. Which superhero would you most like to be?

a. Major Miracle
She saves a hundred lives in less than an hour with her strength, speed, and problem-solving power.

b. Galactic Giggle Girl
Her spellbinding laugh chases evil away, and bad guys leave town when she comes to play.

c. Cyber Saver
She works alone to capture criminals online in electric webs of her own design.

d. Princess Angel
She's always close by and knows just what you need. There isn't any mind that she can't read.

e. Alexis the Adventurer
She can fly anyplace and visit any time to satisfy her curiosity or to stop a crime.

4. Picture yourself on the cover of a magazine. Which one of these do you think it would be?

a.

b. c. d. e.

5. Which award would you most like to win?

a. an Olympic gold medal

b. a Grammy Award for Best Pop Singer

c. the National Award for Best Newspaper Photographer

d. the President's Medal for Teacher of the Year

e. NASA's Most Successful Space Shuttle Pilot Award

6. If an article about you appeared in the paper someday, what would you want the headline to read?

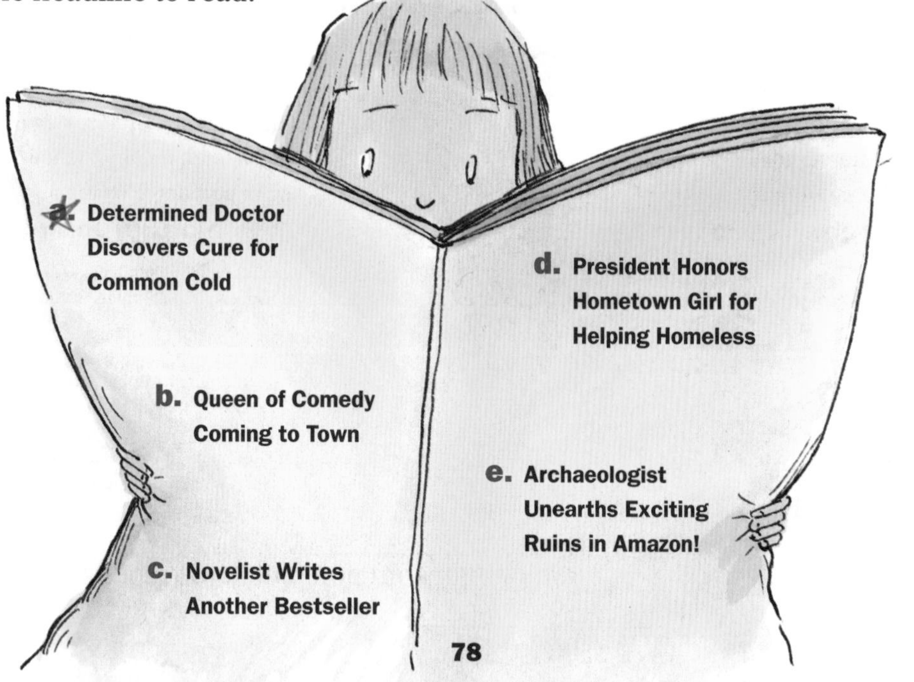

a. Determined Doctor Discovers Cure for Common Cold

b. Queen of Comedy Coming to Town

c. Novelist Writes Another Bestseller

d. President Honors Hometown Girl for Helping Homeless

e. Archaeologist Unearths Exciting Ruins in Amazon!

Answers

Mostly a's

You're a practical girl who's willing to work hard and compete. When you aim for a goal, you're tough to beat!

Mostly b's

You're a fun-loving girl who's warm and carefree. You love company. You like studying with buddies, eating fun snacks, and dancing to your favorite music.

Mostly c's

You're the independent kind with an imaginative mind—a girl who likes to create. You have a style all your own, and you work well alone.

Mostly d's

You have a thoughtful mind and a kind heart. You stick close to home, and you treasure your family and friends above other things. You may dream of being a teacher, a nurse, or another professional who cares for people.

Mostly e's

The sky's the limit for you. You thrive on adventures and look for new things to do. You like to be free to wander and to see whether your dreams can come true.

What did you like best about *The Quiz Book?*

Let us know what you think! Write to

Quiz Book Editor
American Girl
P.O. Box 620998, 8400 Fairway Place
Middleton, Wisconsin 53562

or visit our Web site at **www.americangirl.com**.

Published by Pleasant Company Publications

Editorial Development: Julie Williams, Michelle Watkins
Art Direction and Design: Chris Lorette David
Cover Art Direction and Design: Kym Abrams, Jean Fujita
Quiz Development: Jordan Jacobowitz, Ph.D, Christine DeCassis, Sidonie DeCassis

Some quizzes in this book have previously appeared in *American Girl®* magazine.

American Girl®
The Quiz Book 2
More Secrets Revealed!
Who's your perfect pal?
Can you talk to the animals?
Are you thoughtful?
Are you superstitious?

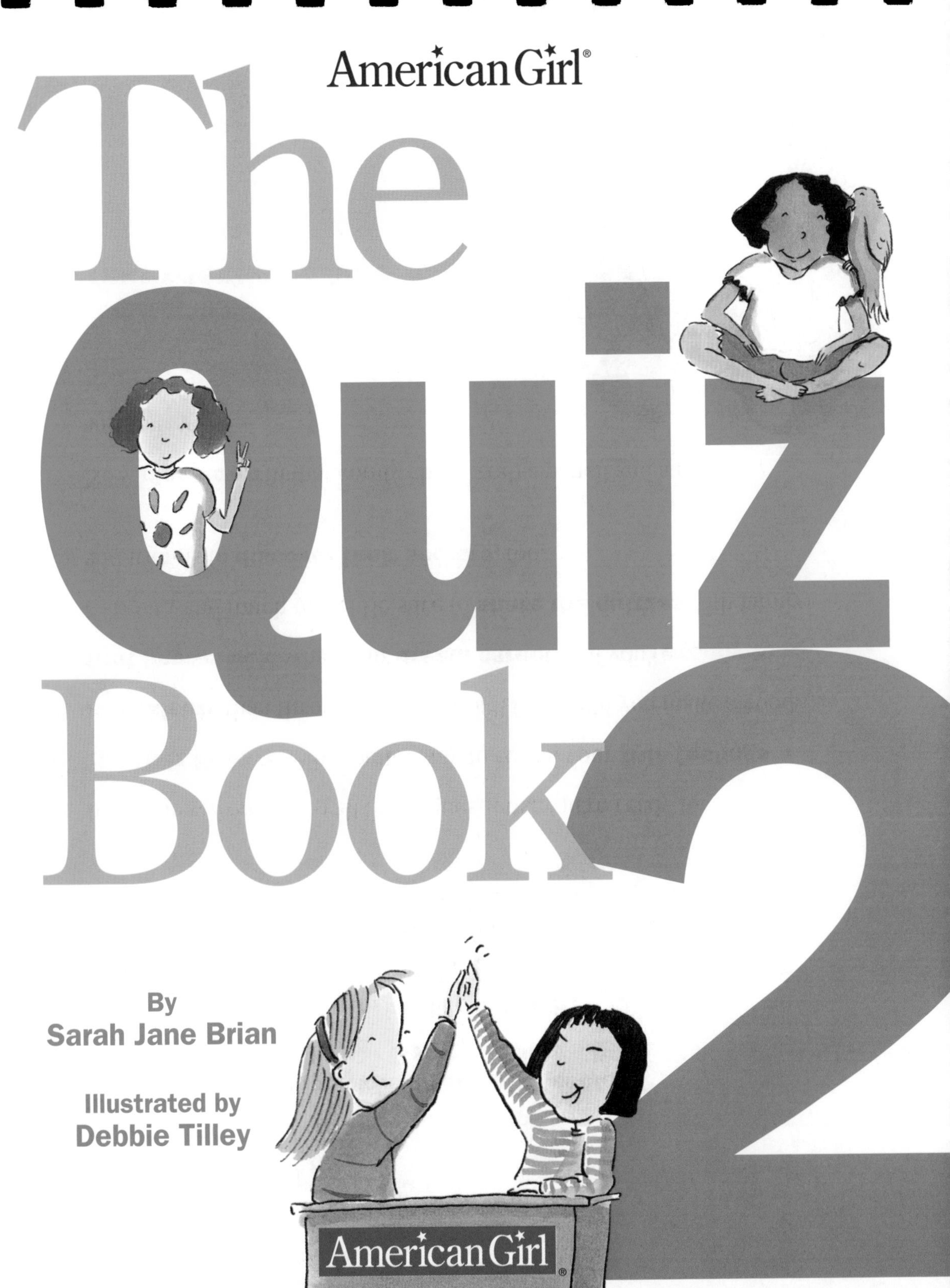
American Girl®
The Quiz Book 2
By
Sarah Jane Brian
Illustrated by
Debbie Tilley
American Girl®

Dear Reader,

Do you love **discovering secrets?**
☑ **yes** ☐ **no**

Do you like to **laugh?**
☑ **yes** ☐ **no**

Do you have a **pencil** and a **comfy chair?**
☑ **yes** ☐ **no**

If you answered **yes** to all these questions, you're ready for **The Quiz Book 2!** What better way to reveal your **true feelings and talents** than through a quiz? You'll find out if you make a good **first impression,** what your **dream career** is, if you're **ready to babysit,** and much more! Be sure to **share the quizzes** with family and friends to **discover their secrets,** too.

Now **plop down** in that comfy chair, grab a pencil and a pal, and **enjoy!**

Your friends at American Girl

Contents

Pup Quiz

If you had a wet nose and a furry tail, just what kind of dog would you be? To find your **pooch personality,** choose the answer that describes you best.

1. When it comes to sports, you have the most fun . . .

a. cheerleading.

b. snowboarding.

c. running.

d. doing gymnastics.

e. swimming.

f. being part of a team.

2. Your dream career is to be . . .

a. a fashion designer.

b. a top executive for a toy company.

c. an author.

d. a movie actor or comedian.

e. a pediatrician.

f. a professional athlete.

3. During the next school election, you'll . . .

4. Your dream vacation is . . .

5. The *Wizard of Oz* character you are most like is . . .

a. the glamorous Good Witch.

(b.) Dorothy, the leader of the group.

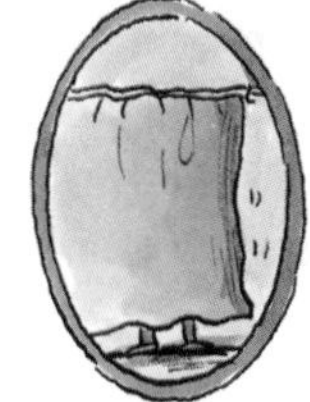

c. the Wizard, who likes to stay out of sight.

d. the funny and fast-thinking Scarecrow.

e. the sweet and tender Tin Man.

f. the friendly and sometimes silly Lion.

6. Your favorite thing to do with a friend is . . .

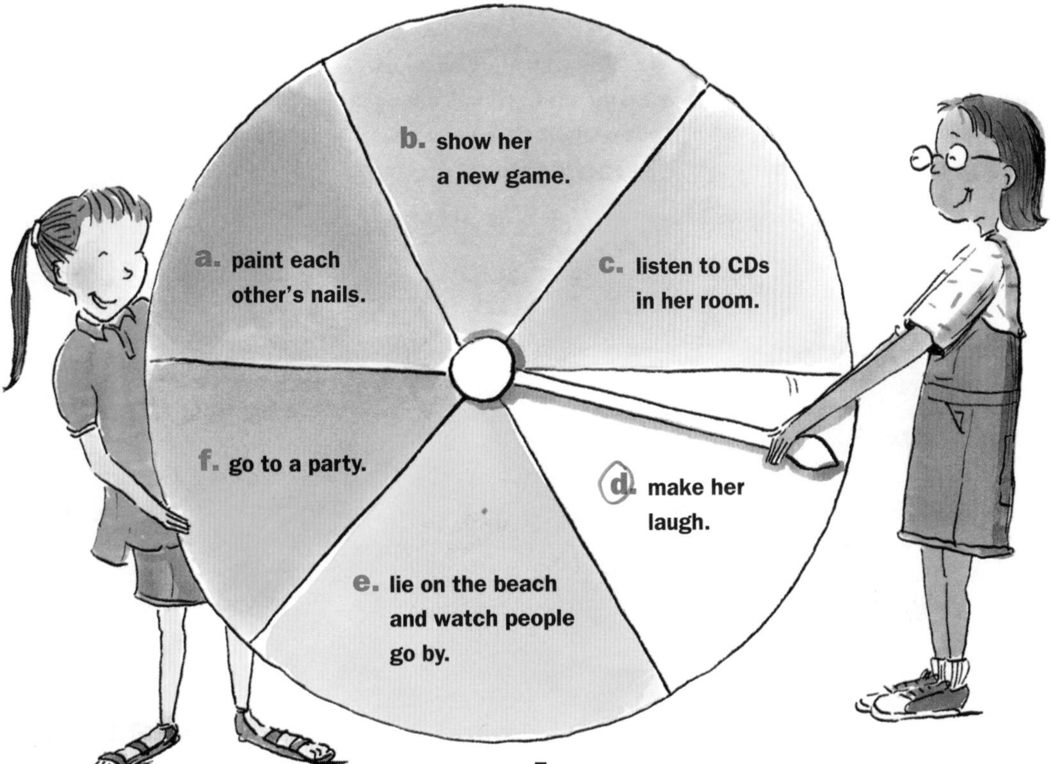

a. paint each other's nails.

b. show her a new game.

c. listen to CDs in her room.

(d.) make her laugh.

e. lie on the beach and watch people go by.

f. go to a party.

Answers

Mostly a's

A **poodle** is the pooch you take after. Like this show dog, you are elegant and energetic. You also may be choosy at times—you know what you like, and you won't settle for less!

Mostly b's

An **Airedale terrier** is bold and adventurous—and so are you! Like the Airedale, you also probably like to be the top dog.

Mostly c's

You are most like a **grey-hound.** Shy with strangers, you are devoted to your close friends and family.

Mostly d's

Your pooch personality is a **cocker spaniel.** Playful and confident, you're a born comedian. You have lots of tal-ents, and you probably love to show them off!

Mostly e's

A **Saint Bernard** is the dog you're most like. You are easygoing, gentle, and calm. You are deeply loyal to friends and family.

Mostly f's

You take after a **golden retriever.** Outgoing and warm, you are a friend to all you meet. You love learning, playing games and sports, and having fun, fun, fun!

How Embarrassing!

Your heart's racing, and your ears are turning **red.** **You're embarrassed!** So, how do you handle it? Choose the answer that best describes what you'd do.

1. When your teacher asks who knows the capital of Texas, your hand shoots up first. "Dallas!" you answer smugly. Wrong! You . . .

a. **turn bright red and vow never to raise your hand again.**

b. **sink down in your chair and decide to study state capitals every night this week so you'll be better prepared next time.**

c. **say jokingly, "Well, I was just thinking they should move the capital to Dallas!"**

2. While carrying your cafeteria tray, you trip and slosh tomato soup on your shirt. Everyone in line starts clapping! You . . .

a. **call your dad to come take you home.**

b. **put on your jacket and zip it all the way up to hide the stain.**

c. **fall to the ground clutching the red spot and pretending you're mortally wounded.**

3. You buy your friend a CD for her birthday. As she's unwrapping it, you remember you bought her the same one last year! Oops. You . . .

a. **keep quiet and out of sight for the rest of the party, then go home early.**

b. **say, "I can't believe I forgot that you already have this CD! I'll take it back and exchange it for you."**

c. **say, "Isn't this great? Now you can play the CD on two boom boxes at once and get incredible stereo sound!"**

4. After strolling out of the girls' room, you notice people pointing at you and giggling. Oh no! A long piece of toilet paper is stuck to your shoe. You . . .

a. run back into the bathroom and don't come out until the bell rings.

b. unstick the paper, shrug your shoulders, and walk on.

c. laugh out loud and point to your foot.

5. You're performing a dance with several girls in a talent show when you suddenly forget a step. You . . .

a. run offstage in the middle of the song.

b. stop for a second until you remember the next step.

c. start doing any crazy movement you can think of.

6. While talking to the new boy at school, a little spittle flies out of your mouth and onto his glasses. You say . . .

a. "Oh, never mind," and go away.

b. "Oops! I hate it when that happens," and keep talking anyway.

c. "Hey! Is it raining in here?"

7. You and your family are having dinner with the new neighbor when you knock over the gravy and it dribbles into the neighbor's lap. You . . .

a. slink into the kitchen and pretend to start the dishes.

b. mutter, "Sorry," and mop up the spill with your napkin.

c. giggle and ask, "Would you like fries with that?"

8. You overslept, and you're really late for school. That means to get to your seat, you'll have to walk in front of the whole class. You decide to . . .

a. ask your mom if you can stay home today.

(b.) walk to your seat as fast as possible and get it over with.

c. interrupt the teacher and joke that you're late because you were kidnapped by aliens.

Answers

Mostly a's

Humiliation Hider

When you're embarrassed, your first instinct is to flee. But all that running may mean that you are worrying way too much. Most of the time, other **people won't even notice** what happened! Even if they do, **they'll forget it** long before you do. And sometimes, making a dramatic exit draws even more unwanted attention. The next time you feel the urge to escape, try letting a minute go by before you react. The embarrassment will ease, and everyone else will probably let it pass, too.

Mostly b's

Bounce-Back Champ

When embarrassing things happen, you try not to make a big deal out of them. Instead, **you deal with them the best you can** and get back to whatever you were doing. You still feel embarrassed, but because you don't show it much, people are less likely to tease you about it.

Mostly c's

Cool Comedian

You cope with uncomfortable situations by making a joke out of them. It's almost like saying, "I meant to do that!" This can be a terrific way to show that you don't take yourself—or the embarrassing situation—too seriously. **A good laugh** can break up the tension you may feel. Keep in mind, though, that there are serious occasions when being a comedian may not be your best bet. At those times, try simply smiling and moving on or, if appropriate, offer an apology.

Perfect Pals

Find out what kind of girls you tend to **befriend.** Follow the arrows to the answers that describe you best.

Start

What kind of band would you want to play in?

country → Do you like having lots of friends or one or two best friends?

hip-hop → What's on your favorite T-shirt?

rock → You like having a friend who can . . .

Do you like having lots of friends or one or two best friends?

lots of friends → You like having a friend who can . . .

one or two best friends → How often do you call your best friend?

What's on your favorite T-shirt?

your favorite team's logo → You like having a friend who can . . .

a cute or funny picture → On a Saturday afternoon, you love to . . .

How often do you call your best friend?

just when there's something important to say → You like having a friend who can . . .

at least twice a day, no matter what! → You think a great gift for your friend would be . . .

You like having a friend who can . . .

be the life of the party → On a Saturday afternoon, you love to . . .

teach you new soccer tricks → You dream of doing this with a friend:

give good advice when you're sad → You think a great gift for your friend would be . . .

On a Saturday afternoon, you love to . . .

play Frisbee in the park → You dream of doing this with a friend:

watch a funny video

You think a great gift for your friend would be . . .

a poster of her favorite athlete → You dream of doing this with a friend:

a diary

You dream of doing this with a friend:

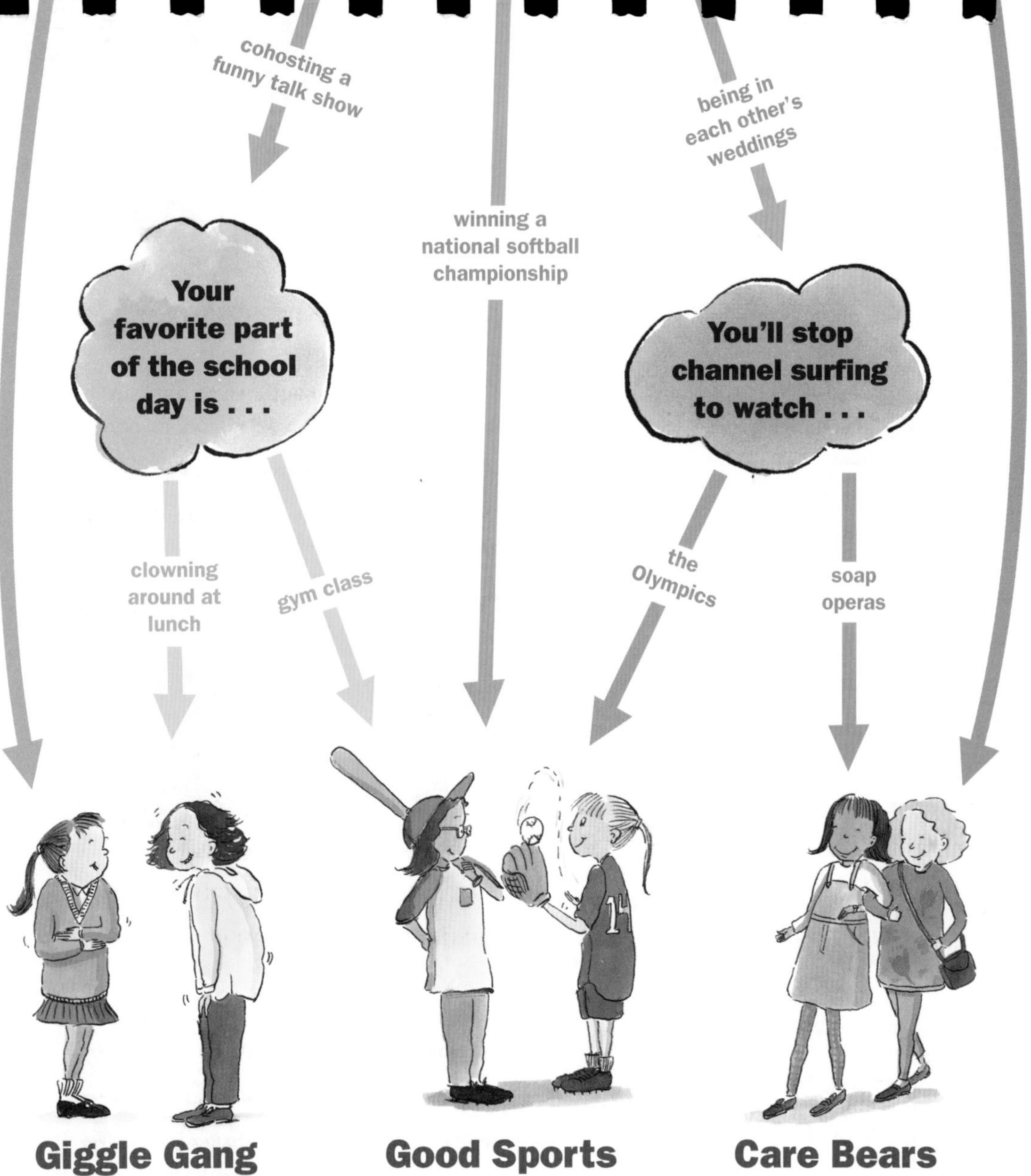

Giggle Gang

You love to laugh! Whether you're in a big group or just hanging out with one pal, you're drawn to funny, outgoing girls.

Good Sports

You like your friends to be athletic and always ready to play. For you, making friends on a sports team is just as important as playing your best.

Care Bears

You treasure the friendship of girls who show they care. Knowing they're always there to support you and share close moments is important to you.

Friendship tip: Don't rule out a friendship just because a girl doesn't match a description from the quiz. If you have lots of interests, all different kinds of girls could be good friends for you. You never know what a new friend might have to offer!

Party Girl

Do you know what it takes to be a **great hostess?**

1. You've finished addressing the invitations to your birthday party, which your parents limited to ten guests. You . . .

a. hand the invitations out the next day in class.

b. wait until recess to hand them out.

c. mail the invitations or drop them off at your friends' houses.

2. A girl who's heard about the party comes up to you and asks why she hasn't received her invitation. You . . .

a. pretend it got lost in the mail, and then beg your parents to let you add a guest.

b. explain nicely that your parents limited the number of kids you could invite.

c. say, "What party? I'm not having a party."

3. It's 2:55 P.M. and your guests are arriving at 3:00. You are . . .

a. double-checking to make sure there are enough paper plates and napkins on the snack table.

b. just about to step into the shower.

c. racing around picking up your little sister's toys that are all over the living room.

4. *Dingdong!* Your first guest rings the doorbell. You . . .

a. yell, "It's open! Come on in!"

b. show her in, then go make a phone call.

c. open the door, hang up her jacket, and sit on the couch talking with her until the next guest arrives.

5. Emily and Anna have never liked each other much. But when they start arguing loudly at your party, you . . .

a. take them aside and quietly ask them to stop fighting.

b. ask them both to leave.

c. cry, "You're ruining my party!"

6. The pizza arrives! You . . .

a. make sure everyone else gets the slice she wants before taking your own.

b. yell, "Come and get it!" and join in the feeding frenzy.

c. push your way to the front to make sure you get a slice of pepperoni. After all, it's *your* birthday.

7. One of your gifts is a hideous green sweater. When you open it, you . . .

a. make a face and put the sweater aside.

b. laugh hysterically and say, "This is a joke, right?"

c. smile and thank your friend.

8. When the party's over, you . . .

a. admire your gifts while your friends wait for their parents.

b. walk everyone to the door and thank each friend for coming.

c. run off to play video games while your parents clean up.

Answers

1. c Since you can't invite everyone at school, it's best to give out your invitations more privately. That way, there's less chance of hurting an uninvited girl's feelings.

2. b Even if you give out invitations privately, someone you haven't invited may hear about your party and want to come. It's best to be honest but kind. Let the girl know the reason you can't invite her, but if you are interested in becoming closer friends, ask her to come over to your house another time.

3. a As the hostess, you should be ready to greet your guests when they arrive. It shows that having them at your party is important to you. Besides, if the guests have to sit around waiting for you, they're likely to get bored, and that's no way to start a party!

4. c Keep in mind that your guest probably isn't familiar with your home. It's up to you to make her feel comfortable and welcome.

5. a Asking your fighting pals to leave or yelling at them in front of everyone will just create more of an unpleasant scene. Instead, tell them calmly how much you value your friendships with them, and ask them to keep their bad feelings under wraps—for you.

6. a Oh sure, you've probably been to lots of parties where everyone just dives right in and getting your food is a free-for-all. But if you want to be a tip-top hostess, make sure that everyone else has what she needs first.

7. c You've heard it before—always say "thank you" for a gift. After all, what counts is that your friend thought of you on your birthday. And saying "thanks" doesn't mean you'll actually have to wear the sweater—just that you are grateful for your friend's good wishes.

8. b The gifts are open and the games have been played, but your job as hostess isn't finished until your friends are out the door and on their way home. Helping your parents clean up is a good idea, too—it shows you appreciate all the work they put into your party. Pitching in also makes it more likely that they'll let you have another party in the future!

The Secret's Out of the Bag!

What do the **contents of your backpack** say about you? Read the report and circle the answer in each box that describes you best.

Backpack Secrets Revealed!

by Reeta Shrestha
Write your name here.

As the school year goes on, my backpack seems to [get heavier and heavier / stay about the same weight / get left at home a lot]. Of course, I'm not hauling around rocks in there, but I always feel like I need to carry [all my schoolbooks, just in case / only the books I'll need that day in class / a few books, though I'm not sure which ones]. All my old homework and test papers from last semester are [crumpled at the bottom of my pack / stored in folders at home / probably around somewhere . . .].

When I have to take notes in class, I reach into my pack for a pencil, and I [find so many I don't know which to choose / find my favorite one right where I always keep it / come up empty]. Then, I need something to write on, so I grab [my chunky ten-subject, fur-covered spiral notebook / the thin notebook I use just for this class / the kid next to me and ask for a sheet of paper].

Of course, every kid likes to make her backpack special in some way. To personalize mine, I [display my entire key-chain collection on it / keep one cute key chain dangling from the zipper / planned to sew on patches, but I never got around to it].

Answers

Now add up how many answers you circled of each color. If you circled mostly . . .

Pink

You like to carry everything with you so that you always know where it is. But let's face it—lugging around that heavy pack is no fun, and it's bad for your back. Plus it's hard to find what you need when your pack is so crowded. Hmm . . . do you think it's time to lighten up?

Purple

Your pared-down pack shows that you are extremely organized. Most of the time, you are prepared without being overloaded. Carry on!

Green

The contents of your backpack are a mystery to you, and you often wind up unprepared. Try making a list each night of what you'll need in school the next day. Then fill up your bag. You'll have a perfect pack in no time!

Sister Act

Are you a **good sib?** Pick the answer that describes you best. Be honest!

1. Both you and your sister always want to ride in the front seat of the car. So when it's time to go somewhere, you race as fast as you can and push her out of the way to get to the car door first.

a. That's me.

b. That sometimes happens.

c. That never happens.

2. Your mom had to miss your dance recital last week, but now the whole family's going to your brother's concert. You're so upset, you sulk all the way there in the car and refuse to clap for your brother.

a. That's me.

b. I might do that.

c. I'd never do that.

3. Your little sister is in your school this year. Whenever you see her in the halls, you pretend you don't know her.

a. That's me.

b. I might do that.

c. I'd never do that.

4. The dinner dishes are clean, and everyone's done with homework. It's time for the usual: you get in a big fight with your siblings over what to watch on TV tonight.

a. That's me.

b. That happens once in a while.

c. That never happens.

5. Your teenage sister is on the phone *again*. You run to your dad to complain and try to get her punished.

a. That's me.

b. I might do that.

c. I'd never do that.

6. You're bored during a long road trip, so you start poking your brother in the arm. It seems like a fun way to pass the time, even when he yells, "Cut it out!"

a. That's me.

b. I might do that.

c. I'd never do that.

7. You are really proud of your spot on a gymnastics team. When your sister goes out for the same team, you're furious! You beg your parents to make her join a different sport.

a. That's me.

b. I might do that.

c. I'd never do that.

8. Aunt Janice just sent over a box of homemade cookies. You're sure your brother will try to nab more than his share, so as soon as the box is open, you stuff your mouth with as many macaroons as it can hold.

a. That's me.

b. I might do that.

c. I'd never do that.

Answers

Mostly a's

Constant Combat

Most of the time, you and your siblings treat one another like enemies. It may be time to call a truce. Talk about "problem areas" that often set off fights, and come up with ways to keep the peace. For example, if you're always bickering about who gets to sit up front, you might want to keep track of whose turn it is to ride "shotgun." And when something makes you mad, cool off before you confront your sib. Stay calm as you explain how you're feeling. Then really listen to your sib's side of the story, and try to come up with a solution together.

Mostly b's

Struggling Sibling

You know you should try to control yourself, but sometimes you lash out at your siblings in spite of your good intentions. The next time your sister or brother is getting on your nerves, take a few minutes to think about the situation. Will fighting or complaining to your parents really improve things? Try taking a break from your sibling instead—go to a friend's house, or just hang out in a different part of your house for a while. Sometimes you need to spend a little time apart before you can be nice to each other again.

Mostly c's

Keeping the Peace

You are doing a great job of getting along with your siblings. Even when a situation doesn't seem completely fair, you trust your parents and siblings enough to know that it will probably all even out in the end. By supporting and understanding your brothers and sisters, you've probably discovered that they aren't only a part of your family—they can also be friends.

Leader or Follower?

Do you **make things happen** wherever you go or would you rather **go with the flow?** Hit the trail to find out.

Start

When you get together with a friend, **who usually invites** the other person over?

a. you (move ahead 1)

b. your friend (move ahead 2)

Who picked out the comforter, wallpaper, and curtains for your room?

a. your parents (move ahead 2)

b. you (move ahead 3)

When you're with a friend, who usually **comes up with ideas** for what to do?

a. you (move ahead 2)

b. your friend (move ahead 1)

Your partner for a school project is telling you what she thinks the project should be, and you can hardly get a word in edgewise. **You have a different idea,** but you're not sure it will work. You . . .

a. wait for her to finish talking, then tell her your idea before you decide. (move ahead 3)

b. go ahead with the other girl's project, since she's so sure of herself. (move ahead 2)

A girl you want to become friends with **invites you** to go ice-skating. You've tried it before and hated it! You . . .

a. suggest that you go bowling instead. (move ahead 3)

b. grin and bear it—you can suffer through skating for a new friend. (move ahead 2)

On a class trip to the aquarium, a group of your friends is heading off to see the dolphins. **You prefer** the jellyfish, so you . . .

a. go with your friends now and hope they'll want to see the jellyfish later. (move ahead **4**)

b. talk a few other friends into going to see the jellyfish first. (move ahead **5**)

Your friend constantly talks about her favorite music group. You **don't really like** the group's music, so you . . .

a. pretend you like it. (move ahead **3**)

b. give your friend a tape of your own favorite band. (move ahead **4**)

When you go hiking, **who grabs the trail map** to figure out which direction to go first?

a. a friend (move ahead **1**)

b. you (move ahead **4**)

You go back to school in September, and everyone seems to be **wearing a new brand** of sneakers. You . . .

a. beg your mom to buy you a pair. (move ahead **2**)

b. stick with the new sneakers you have—you love them! (move ahead **3**)

Trailblazer

You **love to be in charge!** It's great that you are so sure of yourself—after all, you have great ideas, so why keep them inside? Just try not to let your enthusiasm keep you from listening to other people's opinions once in a while, too.

Middle of the Road

You **know your own mind,** and you're usually not afraid to share it. But you also know that you can't always have your own way, so you let others take the reins at times.

Along for the Ride

You're an **easygoing** girl who tends to let others make most decisions. That makes you a fun person to be around, because you're usually up for anything. When you do have a different opinion, though, **don't be afraid to speak up** and reveal the unique side of yourself!

Does Your Confidence Shine?

Do you trust in yourself, or do **challenges** make you weak in the knees?

1. School starts tomorrow, and you just found out your new teacher is Ms. Grimm. She's known for being the toughest teacher in the whole school! You . . .

a. aren't too worried about it. How tough can she be?

b. grill your older sister—who had Ms. Grimm two years ago—to find out if it's going to be as bad as everyone says.

c. plead with your parents to get you switched into another class.

2. At school the next day, Ms. Grimm asks for a volunteer to read out loud. You . . .

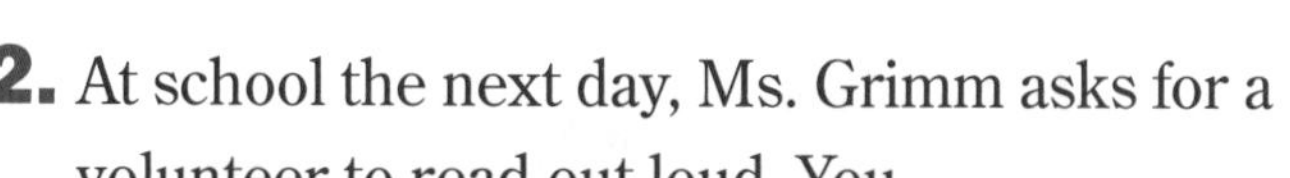

a. volunteer without thinking twice.

b. first scan the page to see if there are any words you don't know.

c. don't volunteer because you are nervous about reading in front of the other kids.

3. In gym, you're playing forward in a soccer game. Your team needs one goal to win. A teammate passes you the ball, so you . . .

a. go for it—you think you have a good shot at a goal.

b. dribble the ball closer to the goal, then pass it to a teammate who is more likely to score.

c. pass the ball immediately. This is too much pressure for you!

4. At lunch, your friends are talking about favorite restaurants. You *love, love, love* Sushi Chalet, but everyone else is ranting and raving about Spaghetti Barn. So you . . .

a. declare, "Sushi Chalet is the best!"

b. say, "I like spaghetti, but I also like sushi."

c. mumble, "You're right. Spaghetti Barn is the best."

5. Your band teacher asks if you'd like to try a difficult solo in the fall concert. You say . . .

a. "It's a challenge, but I think I'm up to it."

b. "Sure, if you really think I'm good enough," and ask for extra help to learn the music.

c. "Maybe next year." You like playing with the group, but a solo would be too nerve-racking—what if you messed up?

6. Your assignment in art class is to draw a bird. You . . .

a. draw a big, colorful bird from your imagination.

b. ask your teacher if it's O.K. to look at some bird photos to get some ideas.

c. ask to go to the girls' room, and dilly-dally as long as you can in the hallways. Maybe class will be over by the time you return.

7. After school, you try out for the lead part in the school play. When you see how great the other kids are, you think . . .

a. I've still got a chance. I'll give it all I've got.

b. Well, I can always be an extra.

c. What was I thinking? I'll never make it.

8. At the school dance that night, you feel most comfortable . . .

a. doing the hottest new dance and teaching it to your friends.

b. dancing the one or two simple steps that you usually do.

c. hanging out by the snack table.

Answers

Mostly a's

Bold and Bright

The word *can't* just isn't in your vocabulary. You're an independent girl who knows that the key to meeting any challenge is to face it head-on with confidence!

Mostly b's

Catching Some Rays

You're confident, but you're also a bit cautious. You like to be prepared before you jump into anything, and you're not afraid to ask for the help you need to succeed.

Mostly c's

In the Shade

It sounds as if you need a confidence boost! Try this: sit down and make a list of things you have done well in the past, like the time you hit a double in softball or baked delicious brownies for your family. The next time you're faced with a challenge, take a look at the list and tell yourself, "I can do it!"

Show Me the Money

Welcome to *Show Me the Money!*—American Girl's
new quiz sensation.
Answer each question below with a friend in mind.
Then read your answers to her to see if you were right.

1. Eat a dozen live worms.
____ **She'd do that.** ✓ **No way!**

2. Sell her pets.
____ **She'd do that.** ✓ **No way!**

3. Move to Greenland.
____ **She'd do that.** ✓ **No way!**

4. Swim in a shark tank.
____ **She'd do that.** ✓ **No way!**

5. Agree not to watch TV ever again.
____ **She'd do that.** ✓ **No way!**

6. Chase a tornado.
____ **She'd do that.** ✓ **No way!**

7. Let tarantulas crawl up her arms.

____ **She'd do that.** ✓ **No way!**

8. Come to school in her pajamas.

____ **She'd do that.** ✓ **No way!**

9. Agree not to talk for one year.

____ **She'd do that.** ✓ **No way!**

10. Have a camera crew film her 24 hours a day for a year and broadcast it on TV.

____ **She'd do that.** ✓ **No way!**

11. Shave off her hair.

____ **She'd do that.** ✓ **No way!**

12. Eat chocolate-covered crickets.

____ **She'd do that.** ✓ **No way!**

13. Sing the national anthem to her favorite pop music star in person.

____ **She'd do that.** ✓ **No way!**

14. Wear orange plaid pants every day for the next ten years.

____ **She'd do that.** ✓ **No way!**

15. Spend a month handcuffed to her sister or brother.

____ **She'd do that.** ✓ **No way!**

16. Go skydiving.

____ **She'd do that.** ✓ **No way!**

17. Wade up to her shoulders in a swimming pool full of snails.

____ She'd do that. ✓ No way!

18. Make friends with the person she dislikes most.

____ She'd do that. ✓ No way!

19. Give up pizza forever.

____ She'd do that. ✓ No way!

20. Live on a deserted island for one year.

____ She'd do that. ✓ No way!

Answers

0 to 6 correct:
What your friend is willing to do for cash is pretty much a mystery to you. Oh, well—money isn't everything!

7 to 14 correct:
You have a pretty good idea of what's important to your pal.

15 to 20 correct:
Wow! Have the two of you been competing on a game show lately?

Pet Check

Test your **pet care know-how!**

1. Can furry pets get sunburned?

- **a. Yes, especially in the middle of the day.**
- **b. No. Fur protects pets from the sun.**

2. Which type of pet is sometimes afraid of the dark?

- **a. bird**
- **b. cat**
- **c. gerbil**
- **d. none of the above**

3. Which of the following is good for cats?

- **a. milk**
- **b. raw fish**
- **c. chicken bones**
- **d. none of the above**

4. What should you do right after you take your dog for a walk on a snowy day?

- **a. Brush the dog.**
- **b. Wipe off the dog's feet.**
- **c. Give the dog some hot chocolate.**

5. How much food should you give a tank of fish each day?

a. about a teaspoon

b. as much as the fish can eat at one time

c. more food than the fish can eat at once so that they can nibble leftovers throughout the day

6. Why shouldn't you line an iguana's cage with newspaper?

a. The reptile may become fascinated with the comics page.

b. Newspaper gets soggy too quickly.

c. Ink fumes can hurt an iguana, and ink may rub off on its skin.

7. How many hamsters should you keep in one cage?

a. one

b. two

c. three

8. Your prize parrot constantly picks at his feathers. He could be . . .

a. bored.

b. hungry.

c. excited.

Answers

1. a If pets stay out in the sun for long periods of time, they can get sunburned in places where they don't have thick fur. Pets with short, white hair and pink skin are most at risk. So rub a little sunblock on your pet's ears and nose—and your own—before going out in the sun together.

2. a Some bird owners even use night-lights to keep their feathered friends feeling safe and secure!

3. d Cow's milk is difficult for cats to digest. Raw fish keeps cats from getting an important vitamin called B1. And bones can cause choking. To keep your kitty in top shape, stick to cat food!

4. b Chemicals and salt used to melt ice on sidewalks can irritate paws, so it's a good idea to wipe them clean and dry them. If your dog's fur is wet, use a towel to dry her off, too. Brushing is a good idea, but it's better to brush before you go out into the cold, since a well-groomed coat will keep the dog warmer. And never give a dog chocolate—it contains a chemical that is poisonous to pooches!

5. b Give your fish as much food as they can finish in about five minutes. The amount of food you need will depend on how many fish you have. If you feed them more than they can eat at one time, the extra food will pollute the water and can make the fish sick.

6. c Newspaper is bad news for iguanas! Better choices are paper towels, carpeting, and artificial grass.

7. a Hamsters like to be alone—if you put more than one in a cage together, you will likely have a big, furry fight on your hands!

8. a Unless he's ill, your bird's bored. Try giving him a new toy or teaching him a new trick. Showing him lots of love should smooth his ruffled feathers.

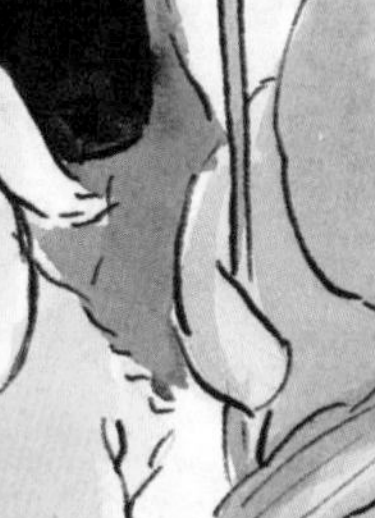

Study Style

Do you learn better by studying words or pictures?
This **memory quiz** can help clue you in to your own style of smarts.

YOU WILL NEED

A **timer** or a **clock** with a second hand and a **friend** to time you

1. Memorize the following list of words for **2 minutes.** Then turn the page.

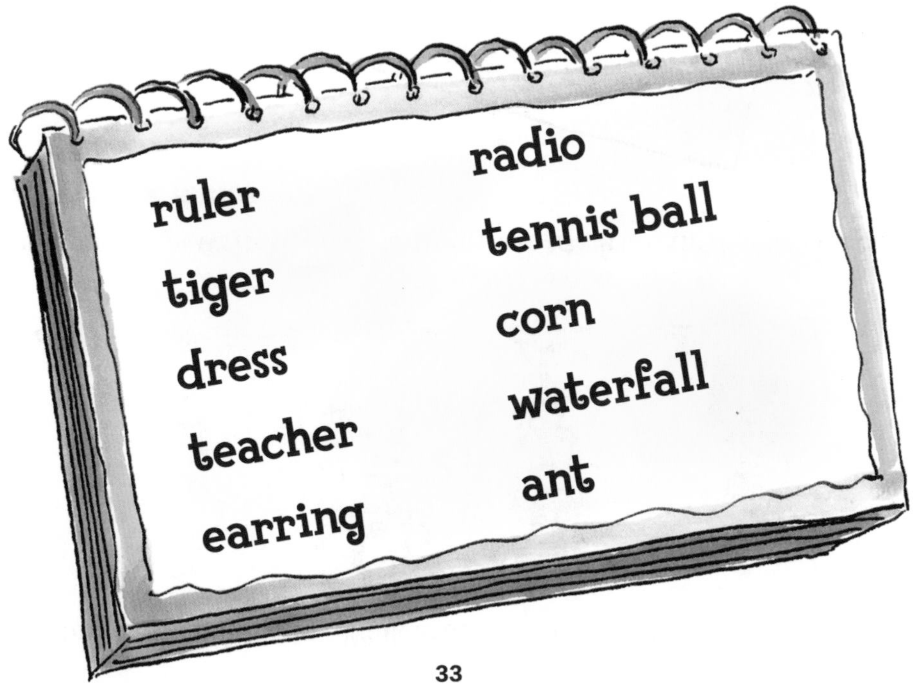

2. Take a break for **1 minute.** Walk around, do jumping jacks, or run in place.

3. When time is up, **write down as many words** from the list as you can remember in **2 minutes.**

ruler radio
tennis ball
tiger corn
dress waterfall
teacher
ant
earring

4. Turn the page.

5. Now study the following pictures for **2 minutes.**

6. Turn the page and take another **1-minute** break. Make funny faces to pass the time!

7. When time is up, **write down the names of all the pictures** you can remember in **2 minutes.**

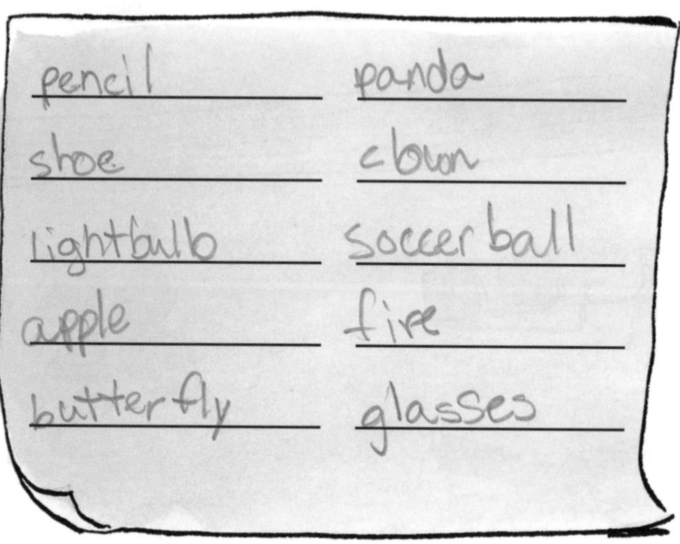

Answers

How many **words** from page 33 did you remember? 10

How many **pictures** from page 35 did you remember? 10

If you remembered more words than pictures, you are likely a verbal learner. That means reading and writing are great ways for you to learn. Rereading information over and over will help you when you are studying. Also try outlining the information you read.

If you remembered more pictures than words, you are probably a visual learner. That means things like pictures and photos help you learn and remember new information. When you are studying, try using a highlighter to help draw your eye to important points. Another tip: pay extra attention to charts, graphs, and maps in your textbooks.

First Impressions

Do you know how to **start out on the right foot?**

Answer the questions below to find out!

1. A new friend comes over to your house. You've never met her dad before, so when he comes to pick her up and rings the doorbell, you . . .

a. **shout, "The door's open!"**

b. **open the door and invite your friend's dad in.**

c. **let your friend answer the door while you keep watching TV.**

2. It's the first day of school. To make a good impression on your new teacher, you . . .

a. **bring her a set of colored pencils as a gift.**

b. **wear a formal party dress.**

c. **volunteer to clean the blackboard.**

3. You're going to a family reunion where there will be lots of cousins you've never met before. You . . .

a. **bring your favorite board game to play with your cousins—that'll help break the ice.**

b. **bring a book to read so you won't have to talk to anyone before they talk to you.**

c. **bring a joy buzzer and some other practical jokes to play on your cousins.**

4. Most of the people at your sister's engagement party will be from her boyfriend's family, and you're a little nervous about being among so many strangers. You tell your mom that you'd like to wear . . .

a. comfy old clothes to put you at ease.

b. a nice dress and your best shoes.

c. your older sister's clothes and makeup.

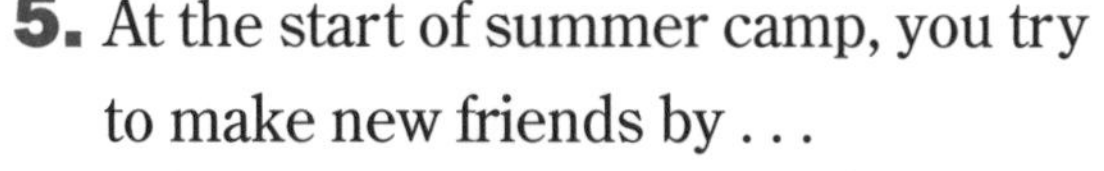

5. At the start of summer camp, you try to make new friends by . . .

a. asking other girls questions about themselves.

b. showing everyone the cool CD collection you brought with you.

c. handing out chocolate bars.

6. Your dad brings you to his office for a visit. When you meet his boss, you . . .

a. look around the room and don't say anything unless she asks you a question.

b. shake her hand firmly and say, "It's nice to meet you."

c. smile and stick close to your dad.

7. When you interview for a new babysitting job, you . . .

a. focus on showing the kids how fun you are.

b. let the parents ask all the questions.

c. ask the parents questions that you thought up beforehand and take notes.

Answers

1. b Your friend shouldn't have to answer the door—after all, it's not her house. Shouting "It's open!" doesn't let your friend's dad know that he is welcome. And watching TV instead of saying hello to a visitor is just plain rude.

2. c Offering to help out will get your teacher's attention and show that you are a considerate girl. A fancy party dress will make you stand out, but it isn't appropriate for school. Giving your teacher a gift may seem like a nice gesture, but it's not really appropriate either, and not necessary.

3. a Playing a game is a great way to start conversations with kids you don't know, which can help you get off on the right foot. Since you don't know your cousins yet, playing practical jokes is likely to make you seem mean rather than fun. Holing up in a corner to read by yourself will make others think you don't want to be friends.

4. b A nice dress lets people know that you want to help celebrate the occasion and that you're happy to be there. You may feel comfortable in old jeans, but the message they send is, "This event isn't very important to me." Wearing clothes and makeup that are too old for you isn't a good idea either. Instead, make an honest impression by giving people a chance to meet the real you—in your own clothes!

5. a Taking an interest in new people you meet shows that you are a caring person and a good listener who would make a great friend. Showing off a prized possession may get people's attention, but you want them to be interested in you, not your stuff. And handing out treats sends the message that you think you have to bribe people to get friends. Once the candy is all gone, the friends may disappear, too.

6. b This greeting is simple but effective, especially when meeting an adult. Look the person in the eye as you shake hands—he or she is sure to be impressed with your respectful manners and self-confidence. On the other hand, hiding behind a parent or avoiding eye contact reveals that you are nervous and uncomfortable.

7. c Let potential employers know that you're eager to do a good job. Ask questions like, "When is bedtime?" and "What are your rules on watching TV?" This lets parents know that you're responsible and you'll respect their house rules. Getting to know the kids is important, too, but your main role will be that of caregiver, not playmate.

Doodle Dictionary

Daisies, dogs, or dots—take another look at the doodles you draw during class. Did you know that they may reveal **secrets** about you? Fill the box below with your **favorite doodles.** Then turn the page to find the **meaning** behind all those scribbles!

Draw your favorite doodles here.

Doodle Dictionary

Now look up your doodles in our dictionary and find out what they may say about you.

Balloon: You are self-confident.

Cup: You're in a generous mood.

Cat: You feel calm.

Daisy: You're in a good mood.

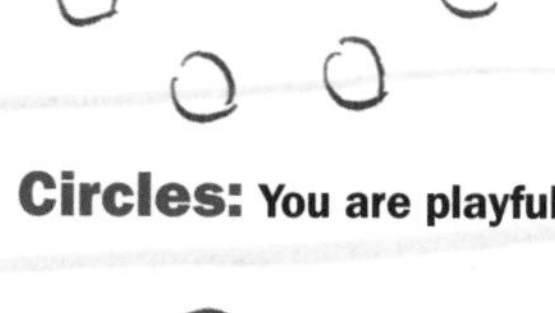

Circles: You are playful.

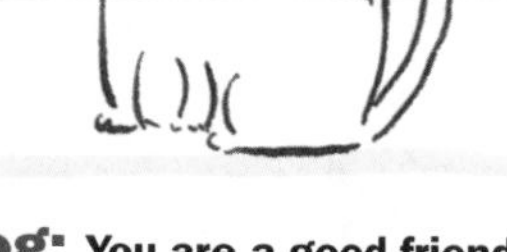

Dog: You are a good friend.

Cloud (shaded): You may be feeling worried.

Dots: You feel nervous.

Clouds (white): You are happy.

Feather: You want to be truthful.

Flowers: You love beautiful things.

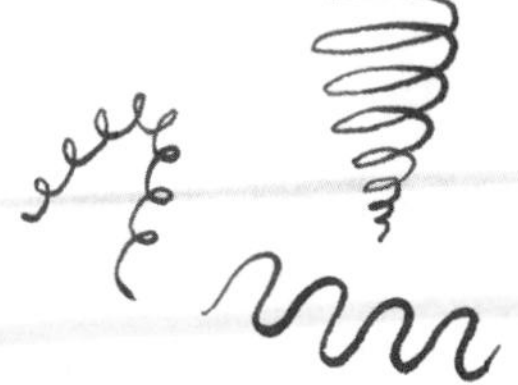

Squiggles: You have a good imagination.

Heart: You're a loving person.

Stars: You feel hopeful.

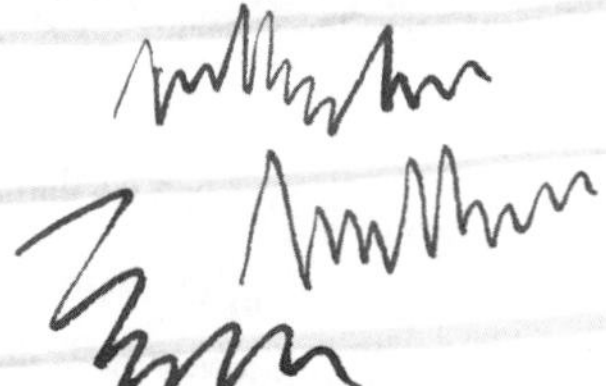

Jagged lines: You feel angry about something.

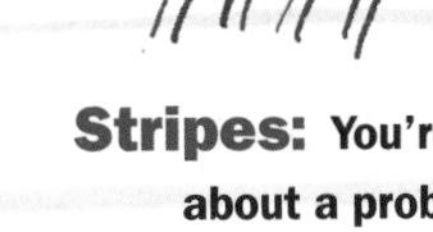

Stripes: You're thinking about a problem.

Plus signs: You always look on the bright side.

Triangles: You have a lot of goals.

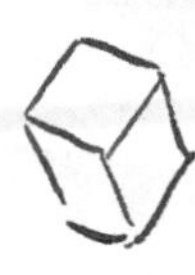

Squares: You like to follow rules.

Tree: If the branches are pointing up, you are reaching for new heights!

Are You Superstitious?

How much do you believe in **luck, wishes,** and other **supernatural stuff?** The answer is in the cards.

Start

CARD 1

You're on your way to a friend's house when a black cat crosses the street in front of you. You . . .

a. **turn around and go another way to your friend's house.** go to **Card 2**

b. **keep walking but wonder if you'll have bad luck later.** go to **Card 3**

c. **reach down to pet the friendly kitty.** go to **Card 4**

CARD 2

At a sleepover, some friends take out a Ouija board. You think . . .

a. **it seems spooky, but you'll ask a few questions and wait to see if the answers are true.** go to **Card 6**

b. **it's great! You've been dying to know if you're going to get the part you want in the school play.** go to **Card 5**

c. **it'll be fun to ask questions, but you're sure it's your friends, not the board, who are pointing out answers.** go to **Card 3**

CARD 3

You've worn the same socks to your softball team's last three games, and the team's won each time! You decide . . .

a. **it's just a coincidence.** go to **Card 4**

b. **the socks must be lucky. You'll have to wear them to every game!** go to **Card 5**

c. **you'll wear the socks again if they're clean, but you won't go out of your way to do it.** go to **Card 6**

CARD 4

At a carnival, you and a friend visit a fortune-teller. When the woman tells you that you'll soon go on a long trip, you . . .

a. **giggle, since you know the farthest you're going is to Grandma's for dinner next week.** go to **Card 7**

b. **start packing!** go to **Card 5**

c. **ask your mom if she's planning a family vacation.** go to **Card 6**

CARD 5

When you break a wishbone after dinner and get the larger piece, you wish for an A on your big social studies test. When you get the A, you think . . .

a. **"Thank you, wishbone!"** go to **Card 9**

b. **"I wonder if the wishbone had something to do with my A?"** go to **Card 8**

c. **"Studying got me that A, not a dried-out chicken bone!"** go to **Card 6**

CARD 6

Tonight is your first school dance, and you couldn't be more excited. Then you notice the calendar. It's Friday the 13th! You . . .

a. **cross your fingers and hope the night goes well.** go to **Card 8**

b. **don't worry about it. You still can't wait!** go to **Card 7**

c. **stay home.** go to **Card 9**

CARD 7

You're checking out the back of your new hairdo with a hand mirror. Suddenly, the mirror slips out of your hand and shatters on the floor. You . . .

a. **wail, "Oh, no! Seven years of bad luck!"** go to **Card 8**

b. **help sweep up the mess—this isn't any different from breaking anything else.** go to **Card 12**

CARD 8

When you go outside at night, you make a wish on the first star you see . . .

a. **once in a while.** go to **Card 11**

b. **every time or almost every time.** go to **Card 9**

CARD 9

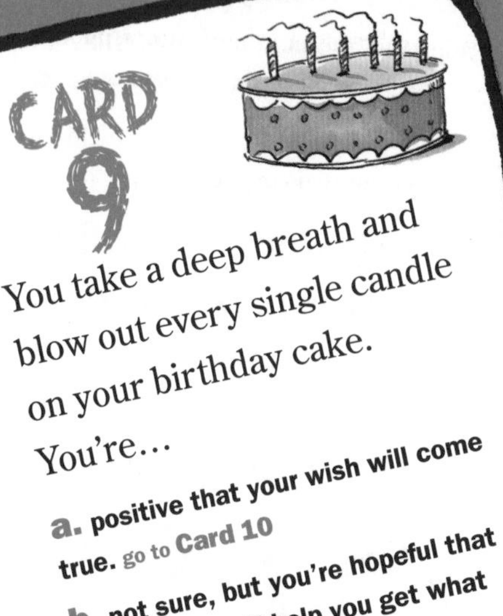

You take a deep breath and blow out every single candle on your birthday cake. You're…

a. positive that your wish will come true. go to Card 10

b. not sure, but you're hopeful that the candles will help you get what you want. go to Card 11

CARD 10 She's a Believer

There's no question in your mind—you believe most superstitions really are true! But if superstitions are starting to rule your life, it's time to change your own luck. Try ignoring a superstition on purpose to see what happens. Go ahead and step on a crack, or just don't follow the advice in your horoscope. Then if you are still worried about superstitions, talk to a parent or another adult.

CARD 11 Wonder Girl

You can't decide for sure whether superstitions are true or false. Was it just a coincidence that a black cat crossed your path right before you missed the school bus? You don't think about superstitions too often, but you probably make wishes and have a few special things you do for good luck.

CARD 12 Keeping It Real

You find most superstitions pretty silly. Maybe you make a wish now and then for fun, but in your heart you don't believe that magic will make it come true. You know that the future is in your *own* hands.

Myth or Fact?

Some of these **old sayings** are absolutely true. Some are misguided myths. Take this health quiz to find out if you know what's good for you!

1. If you have allergies as a kid, you'll probably outgrow them.

- ☐ **True**
- ☑ **False**

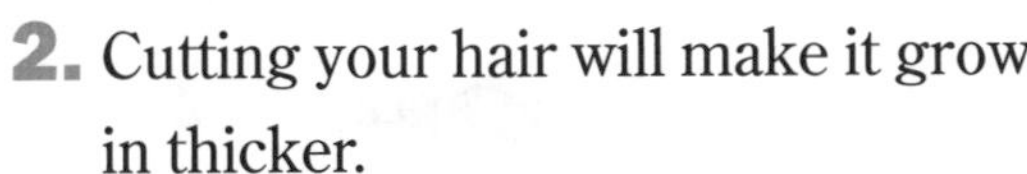

2. Cutting your hair will make it grow in thicker.

- ☐ **True**
- ☑ **False**

3. Fish is brain food.

- ☑ **True**
- ☐ **False**

4. If you swallow gum, it will stay in your stomach for seven years.

- ☐ **True**
- ☑ **False**

5. Carrots are good for your eyes.

- [x] **True**
- [ ] **False**

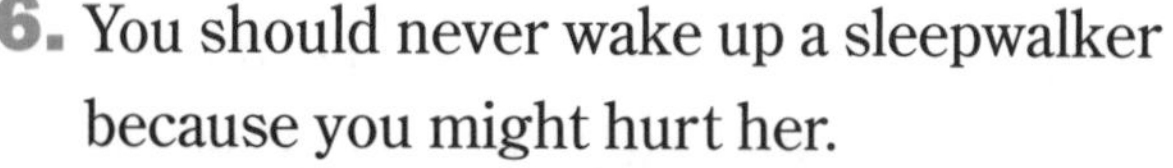

6. You should never wake up a sleepwalker because you might hurt her.

- [ ] **True**
- [x] **False**

7. Eating chicken soup can help you feel better if you have a cold.

- [x] **True**
- [ ] **False**

8. If you crack your knuckles, you'll get arthritis.

- [ ] **True**
- [x] **False**

9. Looking at a solar eclipse can make you go blind.

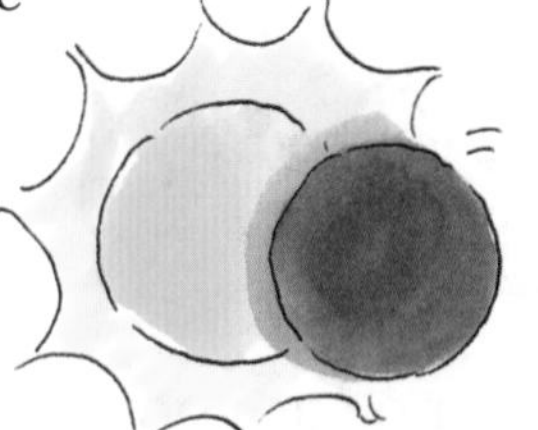

- [x] **True**
- [ ] **False**

10. Touching a toad will give you warts.

- [ ] **True**
- [x] **False**

Answers

1. False. Sorry! Most allergies are never outgrown. Sometimes an allergy improves over time, but it's much more likely to stick with you even when you're an adult.

2. False. The number of hairs on a human head varies from person to person, but cutting your hair won't make new hairs appear. Still, don't despair—a haircut may make your mane look thicker by evening out broken hairs and getting rid of split ends.

3. True. Fish contains zinc, a mineral that can improve your memory. Fish is also rich in iodine, which helps your brain function well.

4. False. Chewing gum will move through your body just like anything else you eat. But you still shouldn't swallow gum—it can give you a bad stomach ache.

5. True. Your eyes need vitamin A to help them adjust to different amounts of light, and carrots are a good source of vitamin A. So eating carrots will help keep your eyes healthy. But all the carrots in the world can't fix a vision problem you already have.

6. False. A sleepwalker is much more likely to get hurt by bumping into something while she's wandering around. But waking her might make her a bit confused. The best thing to do is gently lead the sleepwalker back to bed without trying to wake her up.

7. True. Unfortunately, nothing will cure a cold. However, scientists have discovered that chicken soup contains a chemical that thins out the mucus that makes you so miserable when you have a bug. So the next time you're feeling under the weather, grab a spoon and start slurping!

8. False. That's not your bone cracking—it's a bubble popping in the fluid found in your joints. The fluid is thick, like honey, which is why the sound is so loud. Cracking knuckles may be annoying for other people to listen to, but there's no evidence that it'll cause any health problems.

9. True. Never, never look directly at the sun. Especially during an eclipse, the strong rays can cause temporary or permanent damage to your eyesight and even blindness.

10. False. This myth probably started because of the bumpy skin you'll find on some toads. But we're hoppy—er, *happy*—to report that it's absolutely untrue!

How Do You Compete?

Check off each statement below that sounds like **something you'd do.**

Whenever you get a **graded test** back, you make a point to check how your friends did to see if you got the best grade.

You think it would be fun to be on a **sports team,** but you've never joined one because you're not sure you'll make it in the tryouts.

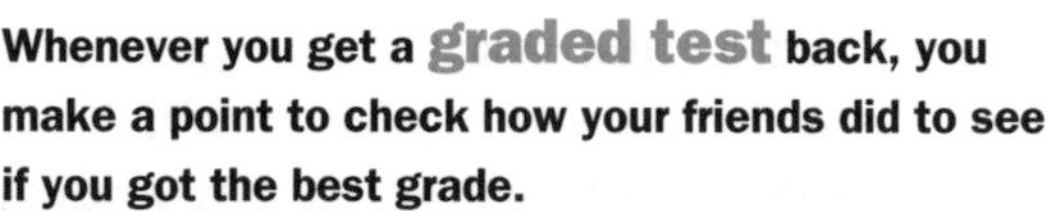

You lose a **game of miniature golf** because you have trouble putting the ball. Afterward, you ask your mom to take you back to the course by yourself so that you can practice putting until you improve.

Another girl is on the **balance beam** at a gymnastics competition. You know that she is better than you, so you go into a fake coughing fit, hoping the noise will distract her.

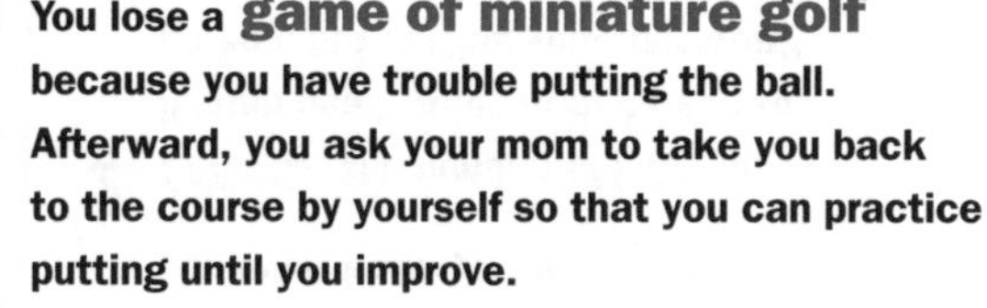

Sometimes you set goals to try to beat your own best, such as making five layups in a row or reading ten more **pages of a book** at night.

Forget the sweat and dirt—your favorite spot at a sports event is **in the stands,** cheering on a pal.

It's your sister's birthday. As she's **opening her gifts,** your brain is working overtime to figure out if her presents are better than the ones you got for your birthday last month.

When you're out for a **bike ride with friends** and someone says, "Let's race to the top of the hill!" you hang back and watch the rest of them go.

It doesn't matter if you **finish a test first or last.** What matters most to you is that you've taken the time to understand every question clearly and check over your answers.

When one of your friends gets a **cool new pair of jeans,** you beg your mom for a pair, too.

A friend asks if you'd like to **play on her Ultimate Frisbee team.** You've never played before, but the game sounds fun, so you give it a try and play your best.

You're playing Scrabble with a friend who is really smart. So **when you win,** you do a victory dance around the board.

You'd rather **play a video game** by yourself than play against someone else.

When **playing Ping-Pong** with a friend, you think it's more fun to hit the ball without keeping score than to play a real game.

You're **playing cards** with your sister when her hand tilts over to the side. If you leaned back a little, you'd be able to see what cards she is holding, but you resist the temptation to look.

Answers

Mostly 

Obsessed with Success

It's great that you try so hard when you play a game. But if winning in all areas of your life is your only goal, you may be losing out. Close friendships become difficult if you are too competitive with pals, and sports and games may lose some of their fun if you can never relax and enjoy them. And if you cheat to make sure that you are the winner, you'll lose the feeling of pride in your victory. When you compete, try to treat competitors as you want to be treated. Everyone will enjoy the game more, including you!

Mostly 

Worthy Competitor

Win or lose, you always try to be a good sport. You like it when opponents play their best, because it gives you a chance to test and perfect your own skills. If you lose, you know that you tried your best, and if you win, you know that you earned the victory. Once the game's over, you don't hold any hard feelings, which means you are ready to meet the next challenge head-on.

Mostly 

Staying on the Sidelines

You usually avoid situations in which you'll have to compete. It may be that you're worried about losing. Or perhaps you'd rather have fun with others instead of pitting yourself against them. That's understandable, but taking part in at least some competition is important. It can help you in lots of ways, from creating new friendships to improving your self-confidence. Just remember that it's only a game, and go for it!

The Nose Knows

Beautiful **fragrances** do more than just smell nice—experts say they can actually **change how you're feeling!** Can you guess what each scent below may do for you?

1. Lemon

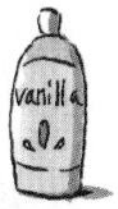

2. Vanilla

3. Cinnamon

4. Lavender

5. Peppermint

6. Orange

a. **banishes boredom and makes you feel confident**

b. **comforts you and makes you feel friendly**

c. **wakes you up and makes you alert**

d. **calms you and allows you to breathe easier**

e. **helps you concentrate better**

f. **soothes you when you are upset or angry**

Answers: 1. e, 2. b, 3. f, 4. d, 5. c, 6. a

The Amazing Sister Predictor!

Are you the **oldest, youngest, middle,** or **only child?** Let me guess! Check off the statements on this list that describe you best.

- ☐ You are superconfident—you believe you can do whatever you put your mind to!
- ☐ You love trying new things, even if you're not sure you will succeed. If it doesn't work out, it's no big deal.
- ☐ You've always felt very comfortable around adults, including your teachers and your parents' friends.
- ☐ Friends often come to you to help them work things out when they have a fight.
- ☐ You like to help your parents around the house.
- ☐ You have friends in lots of different groups, not just one set that you hang out with all the time.
- ☐ Your parents trust you because you've always been very responsible.
- ☐ You try to make sure that your after-school activities (like sports and clubs) are different from the ones your siblings are involved in.

- ❑ You love meeting new people.
- ❑ You often do things to get noticed, such as acting like the class clown or wearing an unusual hairstyle.
- ❑ Whether at home or at school, you always follow the rules.
- ❑ You're your own girl—you like to do things by yourself.
- ❑ You often let friends or family take care of little details. You're not much of a planner.
- ❑ You are a perfectionist—everything has to be just right.
- ❑ You find it very easy to make new friends.
- ❑ You don't really feel comfortable lending clothes, CDs, and other stuff to friends.
- ❑ When you get together with friends, you're usually the one who decides what you will do.
- ❑ Easygoing and flexible, you like to let friends decide what activity you'll do together.
- ❑ When you hang out with friends, they usually come to your house.
- ❑ You're full of mischief and seem to get into trouble more than most kids do.

Now our Birth-Order Fortune-Teller will contemplate your answers and **make her prediction.**

(Ahem, turn the page.)

Answers

If you checked mostly . . .

Blue

You're probably the **oldest child.** You have a drive to succeed, and you often take care of your younger siblings. You also try to please your parents as much as possible, and you like to take charge.

Pink

You must be the **youngest child.** You've learned a lot from your older siblings, but you often focus on being different from them. That way you won't have to compete with what they did at your age. You love trying new things, and you're not afraid to fail.

Green

All signs point to you being a **middle child.** Your older sibs are role models, but you also help look out for younger kids in the family. You're great at getting along with anyone and working out problems.

Orange

Your personality sounds like an **only child,** mature beyond your years. You are similar to a girl who's firstborn. You strive to succeed at everything you do and to make your parents proud. You're a natural leader, but growing up without other kids around may make it hard for you to share sometimes.

What? I Was Wrong?!

Don't be surprised if your personality differs from the typical girl with your birth order. The truth is, although studies have shown that birth order does have an effect on your personality, there's much more to you than just your place in the family. You are a unique person, no matter when you were born!

Are You Thoughtful?

Do you **do the little things** that count? Take this quiz to find out.

1. Rise and shine! You know your mom is under some stress because she's going to a job interview this morning, so you . . .

a. make her breakfast.

b. say "Good luck!" as she's walking out the door.

c. remind her to pick you up after swimming class tonight.

2. While you are waiting for the school bus, it starts to rain. You open your umbrella. You see a friend walking toward you with no umbrella, so you . . .

a. run to meet her and walk back to the bus stop with both of you under the umbrella.

b. share your umbrella when she gets to the bus stop.

c. hope her jacket is waterproof.

3. Another friend is out sick today. You . . .

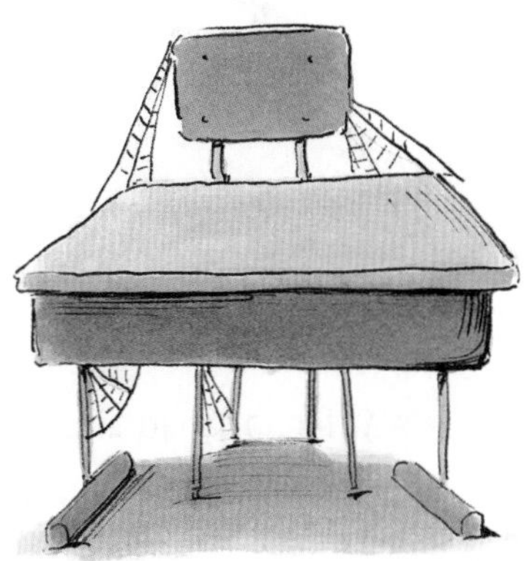

a. pick up extra copies of your homework assignments and bring them to her so she won't fall behind.

b. give her the scoop on homework when she calls you after school and asks for it.

c. borrow an eraser from her desk since she won't need it today.

4. When Dad picks you up after school, you notice an empty hamburger wrapper on the floor in the backseat. It's probably your brother Billy's. You . . .

a. put the wrapper in the litterbag, which is hanging on the back of Dad's seat.

b. say, "D-a-a-a-d, Billy threw trash on the floor back here."

c. ignore it—after all, it's not your garbage.

5. Your dad drives you to the mall to get a birthday present for a friend's party this weekend. You . . .

a. remember some sparkly barrettes she admired the other day and pick them up.

b. buy her a CD by your favorite band—if you like it, she will too, right?

c. can't think of anything, so you get a gift certificate.

6. The next stop is swimming class. When it's over, most of the kids leave their kickboard floats lying around outside the pool. You . . .

a. start putting them away.

b. help out if the teacher asks you to.

c. duck into the locker room so you won't have to clean up.

7. When you look at your planner, you see that it is your dad's birthday tomorrow. You . . .

a. write a poem to read to him at dinner the next day.

b. plan to tease him for being so old.

c. hope Mom gets Dad the same cake she did last year. You love cream-cheese icing!

8. Your sister is studying for a big test tomorrow. You . . .

a. offer to quiz her on her vocabulary words.

b. use your headphones while listening to CDs so you don't disturb her.

c. knock on her bedroom door every half hour to deliver knock-knock jokes.

Answers

Mostly a's

How Thoughtful!

You're a girl who always finds a way to make someone's day. Being around you is a pleasure for others—and they're likely to return the favors by doing nice things for you, too!

Mostly b's

Thinking . . .

You're a thoughtful girl who likes to help others, but you don't always go out of your way or do it the right way. To give your thoughtfulness a boost, try doing more of the unexpected every now and then. Give your mom an after-work back rub, or make a care package for a friend who lives far away!

Mostly c's

Think Harder

You're probably an independent girl who is good at taking care of herself. That's a great trait to have. But don't forget that other people in your life are important, too. Try to think of thoughtful things you can do for friends, family, or people you meet. You'll find that you feel just as good as the person you're helping!

Help Wanted

Tell us a little bit about yourself and your interests, and we'll find **the perfect job for you!**

1. What talent-show act would you love to perform?

a. **funny pet tricks**

b. **a dance routine with a large group of friends**

c. **a skit that shows people how they can help the environment by recycling**

d. **a magic act that uses magnets, mirrors, and puffs of colored smoke to amaze the audience**

e. **a solo that you sing in a beautiful costume you made yourself**

2. When you're stuck in the car for a long drive through the country, you like to . . .

a. **count the horses, cows, and other animals you pass.**

b. **have a family sing-along.**

c. **daydream about how you might make the world a better place someday.**

d. **study the map and figure out the best way to get where you are going.**

e. **draw pictures or write in your journal.**

3. For a summer job, you think it would be fun to try . . .

a. **dog walking.**

b. **babysitting.**

c. **volunteering to help build houses for the homeless.**

d. **setting up Web sites for your friends.**

e. **making friendship bracelets to sell.**

4. When flipping channels on the TV, which show would you stop and watch?

a. **a nature show about lions in Africa**

b. **a funny sitcom about friends getting along**

c. **a real-life story about people who rescued their neighbors from a flood**

d. **a science show that explains how the brain works**

e. **a craft program that gives great ideas for making your own stationery**

5. Which homework assignment would you probably tackle first?

a. read a chapter of a book about dolphins and whales

b. make a family tree

c. write a history report about a hero you admire, like Rosa Parks

d. solve a page of math puzzles

e. write a made-up story that takes place on your favorite holiday

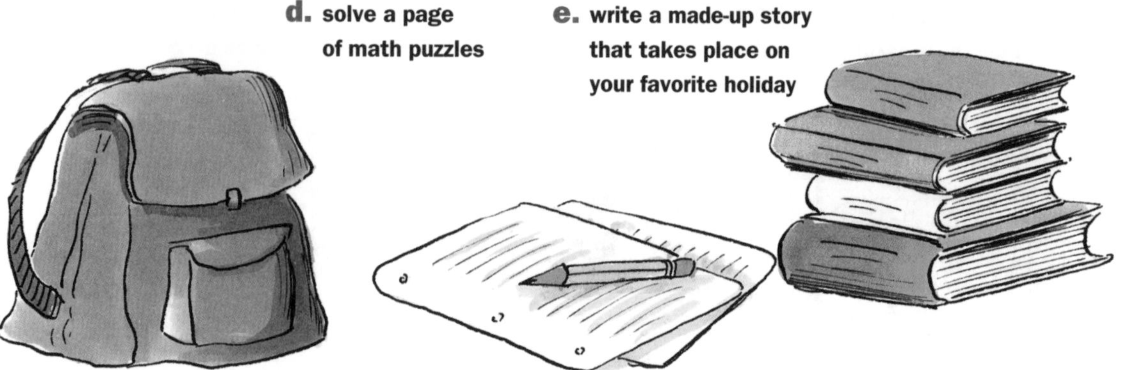

6. If you could redecorate your room any way you wanted to, what would you put in it?

a. a huge pet entertainment center full of toys and places for your pets to climb

b. extra beds to make sleepovers with your friends easy and fun

c. furniture and accessories made of recycled, environment-friendly materials

d. your own lab table for experiments, plus the latest computer equipment

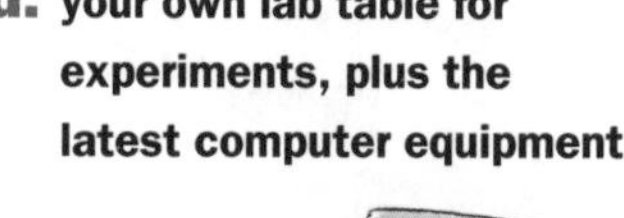

e. a big open space with special lights and a curtain where you could perform your own plays for friends and family

Answers

Mostly a's

Animal Magnet

You are crazy about creatures of any kind! You love to care for animals and learn about their ways. Your dream career might be marine biologist, veterinarian, zookeeper, animal trainer, or any other job that lets you work with animals.

Mostly b's

Personal Girl

Dealing with people gets your motor running. You are caring, friendly, and outgoing. You could shine in a career as a teacher, doctor, therapist—any job in which you spend lots of time with people.

Mostly c's

Dedicated Dreamer

You have high ideals—strong beliefs about how our world could be better—and you are full of hope for the future. Think about becoming a lawyer, politician, reporter, or fundraiser for good causes. With your spirit and dedication, you could make a big difference.

Mostly d's

Science Whiz

You're an intelligent, confident girl who gets a kick out of solving puzzles and finding out how things work. Scientist, architect, computer programmer, and engineer would all be terrific careers for you.

Mostly e's

Imaginative Creator

Creativity is your strength. You love to use your imagination and to express yourself. Your perfect career choice might be actress, writer, movie director, artist, fashion designer, or musician.

The Right Words

When you ask for something, how likely are you to **get what you want?** It might depend on the words you use.

What you want:

You'd like to sleep over at a friend's house tonight.
You think there's a good chance your mom will say "no way."

What you'd do:

How would **you** try to convince your mom? Circle the words below that sound like what you'd say, then find out what it means about your **power of persuasion.**

Answers

a. Not bad. **Offering a trade or a special promise** can often persuade someone to give you what you want. As the saying goes, "You scratch my back, and I'll scratch yours."

b. An **insult** like this won't get your mom on your side—it's much more likely to make her angry. And that means she'll probably turn down your request.

c. It's an **exaggeration** to say that "everybody" gets to do something. But even if it were true, this isn't a very convincing argument because those other people aren't involved here. The question is, why should your mom give *you* permission to sleep over?

d. These words might work. Maybe your mom can think of something that would make her decide in your favor, or perhaps she has a **compromise** in mind. On the other hand, she might be dead set against your idea from the start. In that case, you'll just have to accept the fact that sometimes, "no" is the final decision.

e. Hmmm . . . It seems pretty unrealistic that you'll never have to ask for anything ever again—which makes it unlikely that your mom will be persuaded to give you the permission you want. **Make sure you can deliver** on your promises!

f. Making a **threat** won't help your case. In fact, it gives your mom another reason to say no: she doesn't want to be blackmailed.

g. What's another name for endless begging and pleading? **Whining!** And as you probably know, most people (especially parents) don't like it. If your mom hasn't decided yet whether or not to give you permission, this tactic might just help her make up her mind—to say no.

h. Great thinking! You've used **facts and logic** to show why your mom should go along with your idea. Giving good reasons that your parents agree with can help you succeed in getting what you want.

Are You Ready to Babysit?

Take this quiz to find out if you have what it takes to be a **super sitter.**

1. It's your first time babysitting at little Katie's house. Before her parents leave, you . . .

a. **don't ask any questions—you don't want them to think you're inexperienced.**

b. **go over your checklist one more time. Better safe than sorry!**

c. **start playing with Katie right away. That's why you're there!**

2. Freddie Jr. bursts into tears the minute his mom puts on her coat. You . . .

a. **hand him back to his mom as she runs out the door.**

b. **tell Freddie his mom will be back in a minute, even though you know it will be longer.**

c. **distract him with a funny game.**

3. You and three-year-old Amy are watching a video together. "Potty!" she says. You . . .

a. **take her to the bathroom—now.**

b. **ask her if she can wait. The movie's just getting to the good part!**

c. **tell her to go ahead, and put the video on "pause" until she gets back.**

4. *Boing! Boing!* Maggie won't stop jumping on the bed. When you ask her to get down, she says, "But my mom lets me!" You . . .

a. say, "Oh, O.K." and let her bounce.

b. say, "When your mom's gone, I'm in charge, and I want you to stop—now."

c. start jumping with her. She'll think you're the best sitter ever!

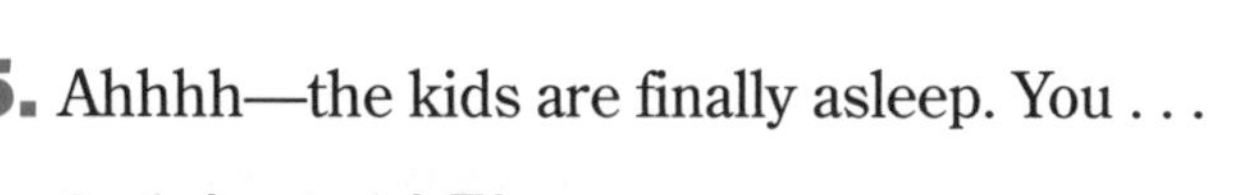

5. Ahhhh—the kids are finally asleep. You . . .

a. study or watch TV.

b. stretch out on the sofa for a snooze. You deserve a rest, too!

c. go through bookshelves and drawers to see what "interesting reading" you can find.

6. The parents have just returned, and you're ready to leave. Trouble is, they don't show any signs of paying you. You . . .

a. go home. They'll remember to pay you later.

b. remind them of your hourly rate.

c. stand at the door and patiently wait for them to catch on.

Answers

Give yourself one point for each answer you get right.

1. b Asking questions isn't a sign of inexperience—it shows you want to be prepared. The first time you babysit, arrive early and get the facts you need—like the number where the parents can be reached, when they expect to be home, what to feed the kids, their bedtimes, and emergency phone numbers.

2. c It's normal for little kids to cry when their parents leave. Luckily, it usually doesn't last long. Giving the child back to the mom will only prolong the tears. Instead, tell Freddie his mom loves him and that she'll be back by bedtime. Don't lie to him, though, if you know she'll be back much later. Then distract him with something new.

3. a When a toddler has to go, she means *now.* Since she's just learning, she'll probably need your help. Stop what you're doing and take her to the bathroom. Praise her for trying, even if she doesn't do everything just right. Help her wash her hands when she's done, and wash yours, too.

4. b Don't go along with any activity that you think is unsafe. Say, "Let's go outside and jump rope instead," or suggest a game to play. Later, tell the parents exactly what happened.

5. a You snooze, you lose! Once the kids are asleep, feel free to read, watch TV quietly, or do your homework. But don't sleep on the job—you might not hear the child crying or the phone ringing. Respect your clients' privacy, too. In other words, no snoopin'!

6. b Babysitting is your job, so don't be shy about asking to get paid. Say politely, "We agreed on $3 an hour, so that will be $9 for tonight. If you like, you can pay me tomorrow." Then call to remind your clients. Treat your job like a business, and they will, too!

How Did You Score?

0-2 points

Babysitting isn't for everyone, and it's O.K. if **it's not right for you yet.** Instead of kids, you might enjoy sitting for plants or pets—they need love and attention, too!

3-4 points

Your heart's in the right place, but **you might not be ready yet to sit solo.** Try being a mother's helper for a while. Watching the kids while Mom's at home is super sitter practice!

5-6 points

Congratulations! **You sound like a pro.** There's one important thing left to do: take a safety course. To find a class near you, ask an adult to call your local Red Cross chapter or visit www.safesitter.org.

What's Your Sports Style?

Are you born to perform, ready to go solo, or part of the team? Take this quiz to find out **what type of sport** may fit you best.

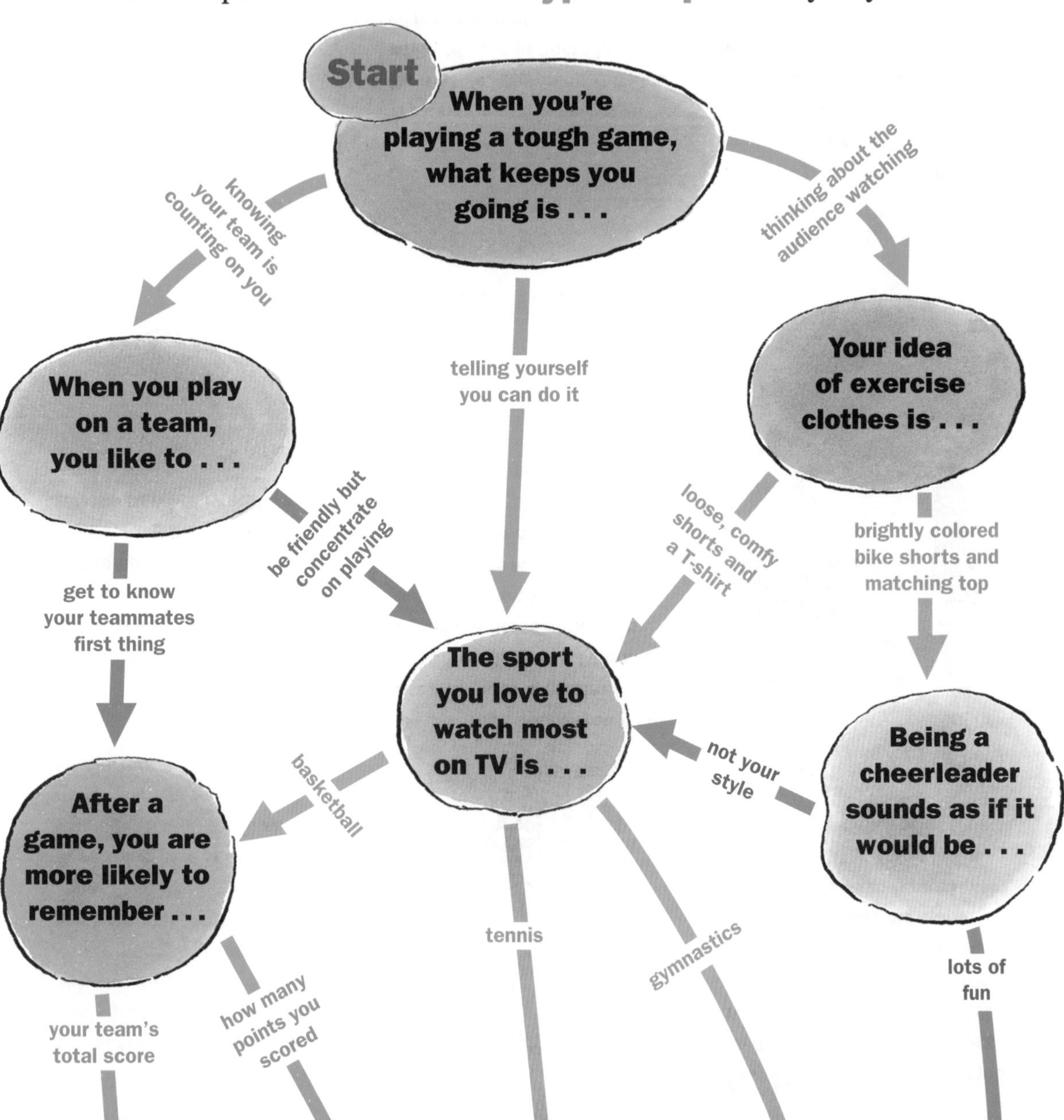

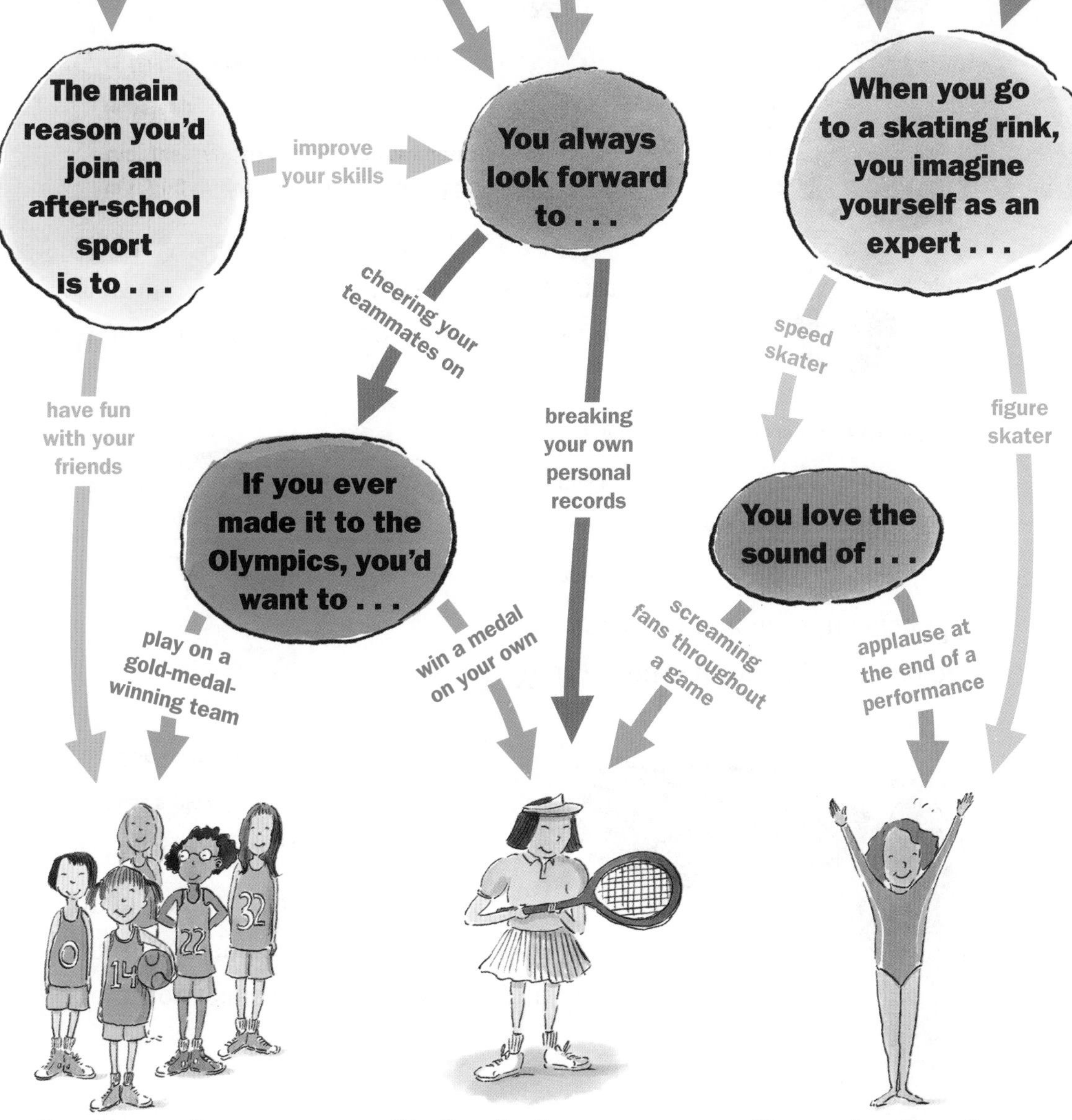

Go Team!

You get a boost when you play sports with other people, whether it's a formal team or just a bunch of friends. Team sports like volleyball, basketball, soccer, and softball are perfect for you. You'll also have fun doing group activities like biking, hiking, and Rollerblading.

Solo Act

No matter what sport you're playing, you focus on being the best you can be. You practice hard, and seeing your skills improve is a great reward for you. When it comes to competition, you may prefer to shine all on your own. Try a sport like tennis, swimming, running, or rock climbing.

Born to Perform

You enjoy sports that involve grace, beauty, and self-expression. Since performing in front of an audience gives you a thrill, try dancing as well as sports like gymnastics, figure skating, and synchronized swimming.

Can You Talk to the Animals?

Your pets may not use words, but they have a lot to say. Do you know how to **read their body language?** Take this quiz to see if you might be the next Dr. Dolittle.

1. Your dog leans forward with her front legs on the ground and her rear end sticking up in the air. She's trying to say . . .

- **a. "Scratch my ears, please."**
- **b. "Let's play!"**
- **c. "Can I have a biscuit?"**

2. Your gerbil is thumping her two back feet against the floor of her cage. Her message is . . .

- **a. "Look out! There's danger nearby!"**
- **b. "Feed me!"**
- **c. "The floor of this cage is really dirty!"**

3. While sitting on your lap, your cat squeezes his eyes about halfway shut, as if he is squinting. This clue tells you that your cat . . .

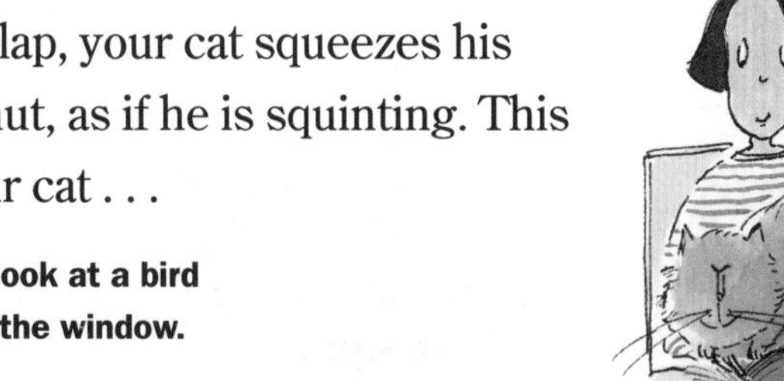

- **a. is trying to get a better look at a bird that just landed outside the window.**
- **b. is asleep.**
- **c. is feeling very happy and relaxed.**

4. Your classroom's pet rabbit lies down with all his feet hidden under his body. The bunny's head is stretched out and down in front of him. He wants you to . . .

a. **pet him.**

b. **take him to the vet, since he's feeling sick.**

c. **trim his toenails.**

5. To let your horse know you're not being threatening, you always approach her from . . .

a. **the front.**

b. **the side.**

c. **the back.**

6. When you walk up to your iguana's cage, his head starts bobbing up and down fast. This is his way of . . .

a. **asking to be picked up.**

b. **getting some exercise.**

c. **warning, "This is my territory! Stay away!"**

7. Two guinea pigs go up to each other and touch noses. They are . . .

a. **cold.**

b. **about to fight.**

c. **saying hello.**

8. Looking straight at an unfriendly barking dog is a bad idea because he may think it means . . .

a. **you're too weak to defend yourself.**

b. **you're afraid of him.**

c. **you're challenging him.**

9. You arrive home from school, and your cat walks over to you with her tail straight up in the air. She's saying . . .

a. **"I'm so glad to see you!"**

b. **"Will you play with me?"**

c. **"I scratched up the couch while you were gone."**

10. Your aunt's bird is sitting on his perch making clicking sounds. He's saying . . .

a. **"I'm feeling friendly."**

b. **"I want to get out of my cage and fly."**

c. **"The hall clock just stopped."**

11. Your horse's ears are pointing out to the sides and drooping down. That means she . . .

a. **is angry.**

b. **feels tired and sad.**

c. **has an earache.**

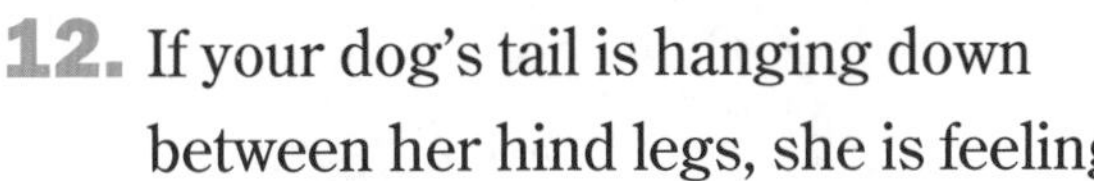

12. If your dog's tail is hanging down between her hind legs, she is feeling . . .

a. **afraid.**
b. **playful.**
c. **relaxed.**

Answers

1. b	**7.** c
2. a	**8.** c
3. c	**9.** a
4. a	**10.** a
5. b	**11.** b
6. c	**12.** a

Snack Secrets

Chew on this—a study recently found that your favorite **junk food** reveals secrets about you. We know it is hard to believe, but go ahead and **circle the snack** that you usually crave. Then turn the page to see if you agree.

Answers

Potato Chips

You are ambitious and successful.

Crackers

You are shy and thoughtful. You treasure time when you can be alone.

Pretzels

Full of energy and adventure, you love trying new things. Routines bore you.

Cheese Curls

You're honest and fair, with a strong sense of right and wrong. You usually plan ahead, and you keep your room neat as a pin.

Tortilla Chips

You care deeply about others, and you hate to see unfairness of any kind.

Beef Jerky

You're outgoing and generous. You're a loyal and true friend who can always be trusted.

Head in the Clouds

Look! **Up in the sky!** It's a bird, it's a plane, it's . . . whatever you think it is!

Head outside on a day when lots of fluffy clouds are floating by. Look at them closely. What shapes do you see? A pineapple? A girl doing a cartwheel? A puppy? In the blanks below, write down the first five shapes you see.

Answers

If most of your shapes were **animals,** it's likely that you are a caring girl. You would make a terrific babysitter, and you are great at helping friends with their problems.

If most of the cloud shapes you saw were **people,** you are probably a very social girl. You like joining clubs, making friends, and spending time with groups of people.

If most of the shapes you saw were **objects,** you are probably quite independent. You like the feeling of accomplishment when you achieve something on your own, such as creating a painting or learning a new computer program.

Let us know what you think! Write to

Quiz Book Editor
American Girl
P.O. Box 620998, 8400 Fairway Place
Middleton, Wisconsin 53562

or visit our Web site at **www.americangirl.com**.

Published by Pleasant Company Publications

Editorial Development: Julie Williams, Michelle Watkins
Art Direction and Design: Chris Lorette David
Production: Kendra Pulvermacher and Janette Sowinski
Quiz Development: Gregory Smith, Ph.D.

Some quizzes in this book have previously appeared in *American Girl*® magazine.

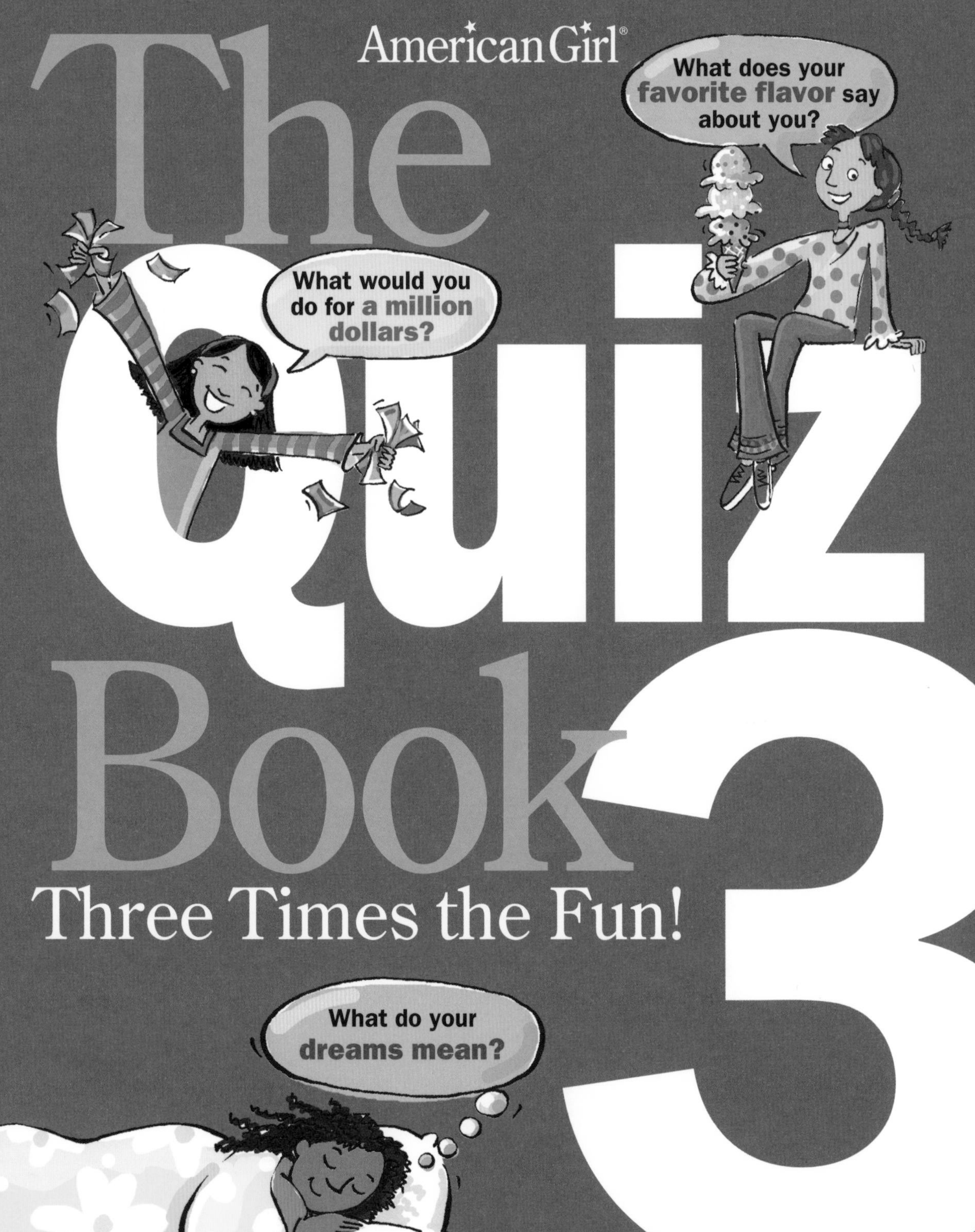
American Girl
The Quiz Book 3
What does your favorite flavor say about you?
What would you do for a million dollars?
Three Times the Fun!
What do your dreams mean?

Three Times the Fun!

By
Brette Sember

Illustrated by
Lauren Scheuer

American Girl

Dear Reader,

You asked for it! You begged for it! And now it's here— **Quiz Book 3** with **26** all-new, fun **quizzes** to help you learn even more about **you.**

What kind of **friend** are you? How do you spend your **free time?** Are you **stressed out?** Do you hold a **grudge?** Your answers to the questions in this book will reveal more about the true you!

You'll also find quizzes that help you see how much you know about your **friends and family** and about yourself when you were little. When you're done, quiz a **friend,** quiz **your sister,** quiz **everyone you know . . .** and then, quiz yourself again and again!

Until next time—

Your friends at American Girl

Contents

Hue Do You Do?

Your **favorite color** reveals a lot about you. Circle your fave-colored tee, then turn the page to see how it colors your personality.

- ❑ Red
- ❑ Yellow
- ❑ Blue
- ❑ Green
- ❑ Orange
- ❑ Black
- ❑ White
- ❑ Brown
- ❑ Purple
- ❑ Pink

Answers

Red: If you love red, you're all about excitement. You love to be at the center of the action. Your feelings can be very intense.

Yellow: You are carefree. You always look on the bright side of things. You also love to feel warm and cozy.

Blue: You tend to appreciate some time alone, but you can be a really loyal friend. You are very organized.

Green: You're full of energy and ready to try new things. You also like to look on the bright side of things.

Orange: You're pretty satisfied with your life. You like to get things accomplished and often try to do good deeds.

Black: You are serious, and you make a good leader. You like to be in charge and organize things.

White: You're very honest, and you try to do things the right way. You like to keep your things neat and clean.

Brown: You think that when you get right down to it, you're a pretty decent person. People can count on you, and you make a very dependable friend.

Purple: You are creative and witty. You love to fantasize. In your dreams, you are a princess!

Pink: You have a very calm personality. Your feelings are very important to you and can be easily hurt. You love to daydream.

Rock Around the Clock

Are you **bright-eyed in the morning, nifty in the afternoon,** or a **night creature?**
To find out, pick the answer that fits you best.

1. If it were up to you, you would automatically wake up at . . .

   a. **7 A.M. You've got things to do, people to see, and places to go!**

   b. **8:30 A.M. What's the hurry?**

   c. **10 A.M. A growing girl needs her sleep, you know!**

2. Be it a cute cat sitting in a neighbor's window or a funny joke someone tells you, you are most likely to remember details about . . .

   a. **your trip to school in the morning.**

   b. **your trip home from school in the afternoon.**

   c. **your bike ride after dinner.**

3. You have a big math test on Friday. You've studied and you're ready to ace the test, but you would do best if it were scheduled for . . .

   a. **first period—bright and early while your brain is fresh.**

   b. **fifth period—right after you fill up on brain food.**

   c. **last period—when your brain is really humming along.**

4. Yakety-yak. You're most likely to chat up a storm . . .

a. first thing in the morning when you see your friends at school.

b. hanging out after school.

c. at the dinner table or on the phone before bedtime.

5. At a slumber party, you're usually . . .

a. the first to crash.

b. dozing off right about the same time as the other guests.

c. the last one to fall asleep.

6. Everyone gets a little grumpy now and then. For you, it happens mostly . . .

a. at night before bedtime.

b. Who, me? Grumpy?

c. in the early morning after waking up.

7. To make sure you have lots of energy, you schedule your tennis lessons on Saturdays during the . . .

a. morning.

b. afternoon.

c. evening.

8. You have to memorize and recite the poem "Where the Sidewalk Ends" for English class next week, so you practice . . .

a. every morning—things sink in better then.

b. after school, when you're plowing through the rest of your homework.

c. in the evening, because you can concentrate best then.

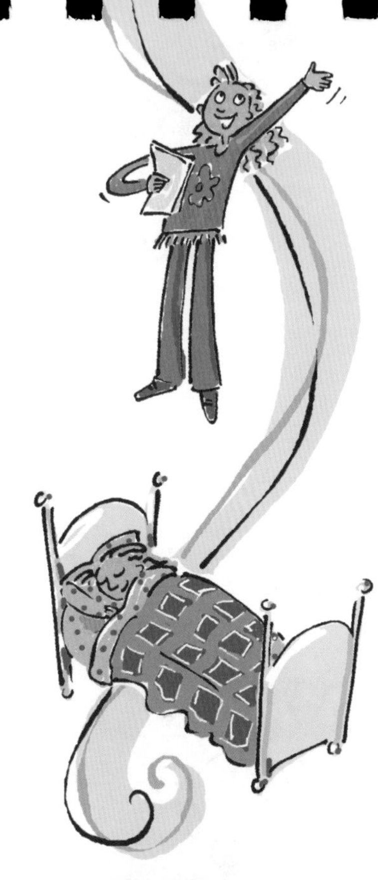

9. All good things must come to an end. When it's not a school night, you hit the sack at . . .

a. 9 P.M.—like clockwork!

b. 10 P.M.—after all the good shows on TV are over.

c. 11 P.M.—zonked out with the light on is more like it.

Answers

Mostly a's

Morning Mover

Even if you're not always up before the rooster crows, mornings are when you're at your perkiest.

Mostly b's

Afternoon Ace

It takes you a while to warm up and get into the day. Afternoons are when you're at your best.

Mostly C's

Night Owl

The moon and the stars are your brightest lights. You're not fully in gear until evening falls.

Baby Talk

How much do you know about **yourself as a baby?**
Answer the questions and get a parent to correct them for you.

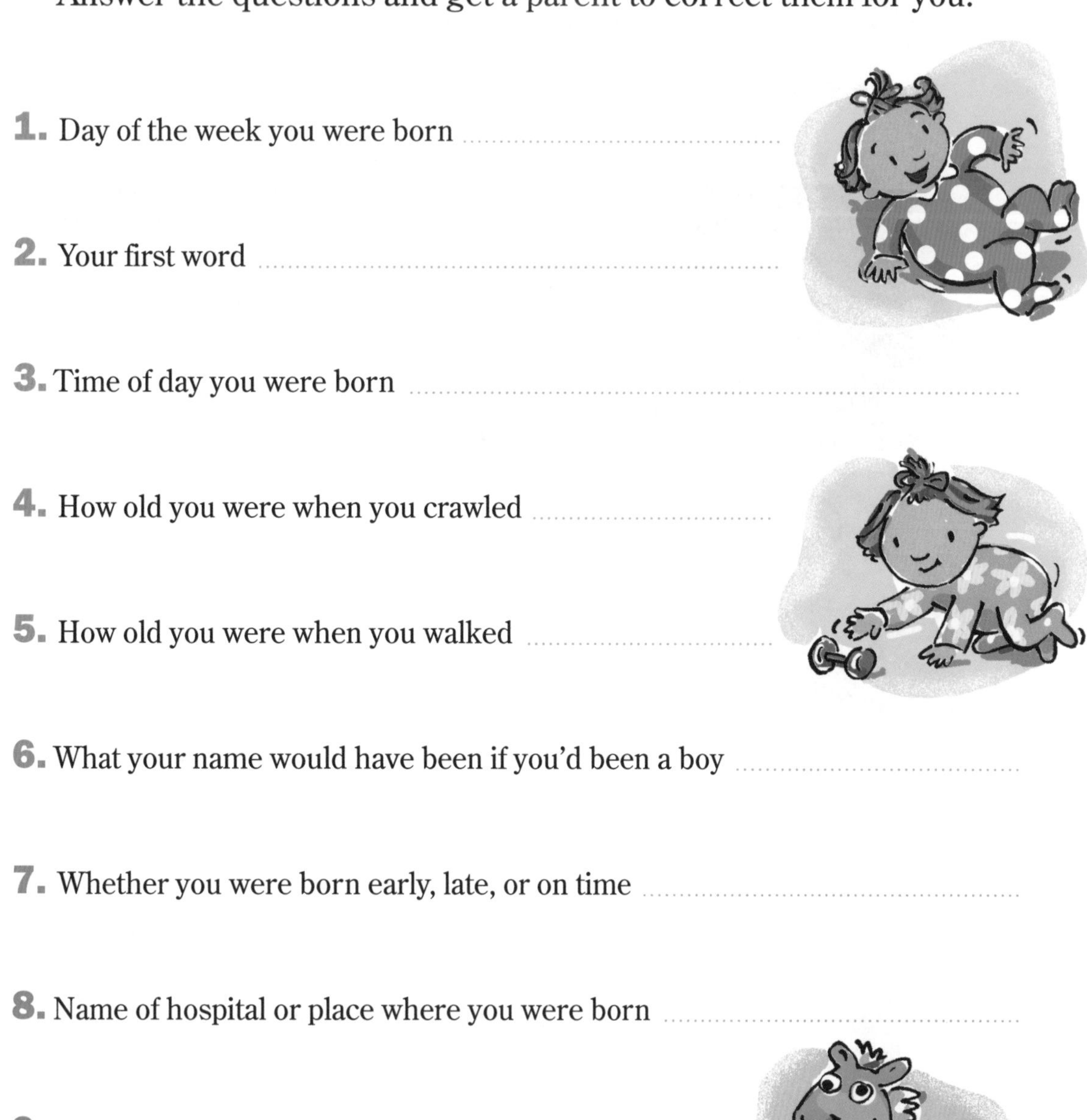

1. Day of the week you were born ....

2. Your first word ....

3. Time of day you were born ....

4. How old you were when you crawled ....

5. How old you were when you walked ....

6. What your name would have been if you'd been a boy ....

7. Whether you were born early, late, or on time ....

8. Name of hospital or place where you were born ....

9. Your favorite baby toy ....

10. How old you were when you got your first tooth ....

11. Why your parents picked your name ....

12. Where your parents lived when you were a baby ....

13. What color your hair was when you were born ....

14. Your favorite way to be put to sleep ....

15. The color of your baby blanket ....

16. Your favorite lullaby ....

17. Whether you were a good sleeper, an O.K. sleeper, or awake all night every night ....

18. Your favorite baby food ....

19. How much you weighed at birth ....

20. How long you were at birth ....

Scoring

Give yourself **1 point** for each correct answer.

15 to 20 points

History Buff

You know a lot about your early years. You must have read that baby memory book and enjoyed a lot of "When you were a baby . . ." stories.

8 to 14 points

Goo-Goo Good

You already have many of the facts about your beginnings. There are probably some stories you haven't heard, though. Find out what else your parents or relatives can tell you about you!

0 to 7 points

Ba-Ba Baffled!

There's so much to learn about your babyhood. Go through the questions with your parents and ask them to help you learn more about sweet little you!

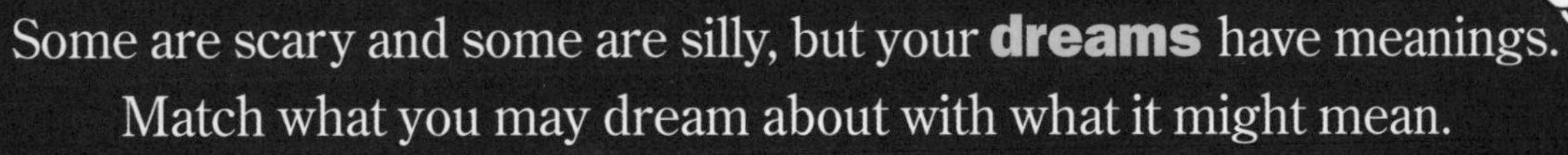

Sweet Dreams

Some are scary and some are silly, but your **dreams** have meanings. Match what you may dream about with what it might mean.

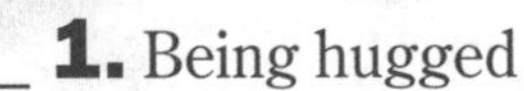

__ **1.** Being hugged

__ **2.** Falling

__ **3.** A car

__ **4.** Flying

__ **5.** A tornado

__ **6.** Being lost or trapped

__ **7.** An animal

__ **8.** Being naked in public

__ **9.** Being chased

__ **10.** Being late for school or not ready for a test

__ **11.** A house

a. You're afraid of something.

b. You're nervous.

c. This symbol represents you.

d. You feel good or confident about something.

e. This symbol stands for part of your personality.

f. You feel anxious or unprepared.

g. You don't feel in control.

h. You feel exposed or vulnerable.

i. You want to be closer to a person.

j. You're confused.

k. What happens with this symbol stands for what's happening with you.

Answers

1. Being hugged, i. When you dream about hugging, it means you want to be closer to the person you are hugging or you want to be more like him or her.

2. Falling, b. If you dream you're falling, you probably feel nervous about something in your life—for example, a science project that you can't seem to get finished.

3. Car, k. What is happening with a car in your dream stands for something happening with you. For example, if the car is going in a new direction, you might be trying some new things or meeting new people.

4. Flying, d. Flying means you feel good or confident about something. This kind of dream can also mean you feel free.

5. Tornado, g. A dream about a tornado symbolizes that you feel lack of control over something in your life. You might be under too much pressure or going through something emotional like a big change.

6. Being lost or trapped, j. A dream in which you're lost or trapped means you're feeling confused about something in your life, such as an argument you and your best friend had.

7. Animal, e. Animals that you dream about stand for parts of your personality. Think about the animal in the dream and how you are like it. A dream about an ostrich might be about your shy side, while a dream about a graceful swan might be about your dancing ability.

8. Being naked in public, h. This kind of dream means you feel exposed or vulnerable about something. For example, maybe you're worried about forgetting your lines in the school play.

9. Being chased, a. Dreams where you're being chased mean that there is something in your life you are afraid of, such as a big test, moving to a new town, or a parent losing a job. Your dream might be giving your mind a chance to face the fear and find the courage to get through it.

10. Being late for school/not ready for a test, f. This kind of dream means you feel unprepared for something or you are anxious about something. Try making a list of what you need to do before going to bed to ease your mind.

11. House, c. Dreams about houses or rooms in houses are really about you. The room you dream about represents a part of your life. A house dream might mean you're thinking carefully about something that you're not so sure about.

Do You Want to Be a Millionaire?

What would **you** do for a million dollars?

1. Give up the computer forever.

   _____ **No problem** _____ **No way!**

2. Eat deep-fried octopus dipped in hot sauce.

   _____ **No problem** _____ **No way!**

3. Share your room with a three-year-old for a year.

   _____ **No problem** _____ **No way!**

4. Get a tattoo that says, "Boys are smarter than girls."

   _____ **No problem** _____ **No way!**

5. Cook dinner every night for six months.

   _____ **No problem** _____ **No way!**

6. Stick your arm into a swarming beehive.

   _____ **No problem** _____ **No way!**

7. Walk to the North Pole.

_____ No problem _____ No way!

8. Drink goat's milk.

_____ No problem _____ No way!

9. Listen only to opera music for the next ten years.

_____ No problem _____ No way!

10. Go bungee jumping.

_____ No problem _____ No way!

11. Walk barefoot through a ditch filled with big, slimy slugs.

_____ No problem _____ No way!

12. Not talk to your best friend for three months.

_____ No problem _____ No way!

13. Tap dance to "Yankee Doodle Dandy" in front of the whole school, wearing an orange sequined leotard and green polka-dot tights.

_____ No problem _____ No way!

14. Hang glide over an active volcano.

_____ **No problem** _____ **No way!**

15. Chew a piece of bubble gum that was stuck to the bottom of someone's shoe.

_____ **No problem** _____ **No way!**

16. Publish your diary in the newspaper.

_____ **No problem** _____ **No way!**

17. Let your parents pick out your clothes for the rest of your life.

_____ **No problem** _____ **No way!**

Scoring

1 or more "No problem"s

Congratulations! You got the cash. But was it worth it? Do you know where that bubble gum has been?

0 "No problem"s

Your good sense is priceless! Is there ANYTHING you'd do for a million bucks? Now, that's a million-dollar question!

Predict Your Friend's Future

Get out your crystal ball and **look into the future.** Where will your best bud be? What will she do? How will she live? Guess your friend's hopes and dreams, then have her check your answers.

1. Your friend's dream home is . . .

a. **a loft apartment in a big city.**

b. **a house with a white picket fence and a big yard.**

c. **a motor home, cruising from spot to spot.**

2. After she graduates from high school, she would like to . . .

a. **travel overseas.**

b. **start a rock band.**

c. **hit the books in college.**

d. **marry her high-school sweetheart.**

e. **train for the Olympics.**

3. She would love a job as . . .

a. a lawyer standing up for people's rights.

b. a gourmet chef with a chain of 4-star restaurants, a cooking show, and her own brand of spaghetti sauce.

c. a greeting card illustrator who cares to draw the very best.

d. an investigative reporter who searches relentlessly for the truth.

e. a psychic advisor to the nation's president.

f. a wildlife expert who specializes in protecting endangered manatees.

4. Her house will have . . .

a. lots of animal prints, candles, and fountains.

b. plenty of lace, pillows, and flowers.

c. movable walls, a retractable roof, videophones, and all kinds of other high-tech gadgets.

d. just the basics—she would spend her money on other things.

5. When you look in her fridge, you'll find . . .

a. an empty pizza box and a jar of mayo.

b. sushi, taco fixin's, take-out Chinese, and other ethnic foods.

c. nothing but veggies.

d. 33 flavors of ice cream.

6. As a grown-up, she'll live . . .

a. **with her husband and kids.**

b. **with a collection of pets.**

c. **with some nutty roommates.**

d. **by herself—and love it!**

e. **on the road, seeing the country.**

7. Her favorite hangout will be . . .

a. **a trendy corner coffee shop.**

b. **a noisy soccer field.**

c. **the beach at sunset.**

d. **her own backyard.**

e. **a funky art museum.**

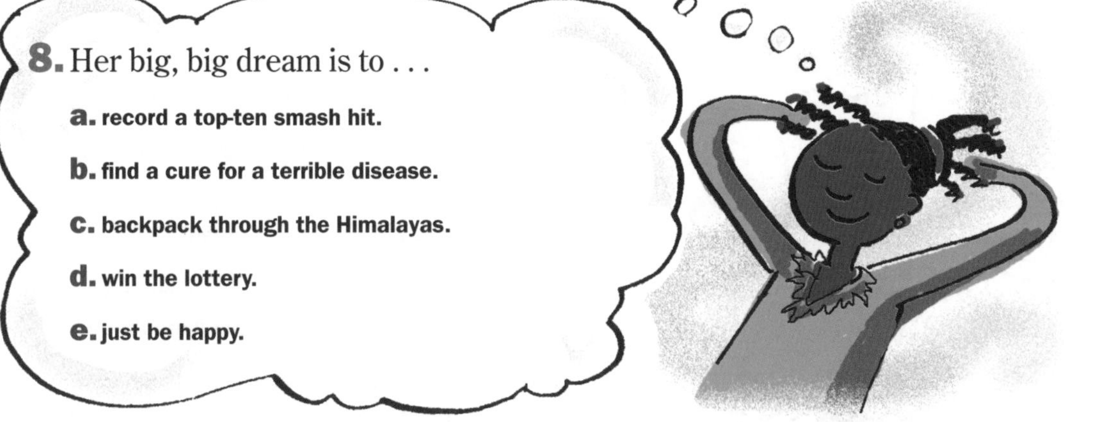

8. Her big, big dream is to . . .

a. **record a top-ten smash hit.**

b. **find a cure for a terrible disease.**

c. **backpack through the Himalayas.**

d. **win the lottery.**

e. **just be happy.**

9. Her first set of wheels will be a . . .

a. big red pickup truck.

b. racy red convertible.

c. cute green VW bug.

d. mountain bike.

e. new electric car that doesn't guzzle gas.

10. On her 21st birthday, she will . . .

a. catch a shuttle to the moon to celebrate.

b. have cake and ice cream with family and friends.

c. plan a Big Birthday Blowout Bash and invite 100 of her closest friends.

d. tell everyone not to make a fuss but then be surprised with a party.

Scoring

Give yourself **1 point** for each correct answer.

0 to 3 points

Unknown Quantity

Your friend has dreams and plans you never knew about. Take some time to discuss the wishes and hopes both of you have for the future.

4 to 7 points

Friends for Sure

You're clued in to what she wants. Does she know what you dream about? Have her take the quiz now!

8 to 10 points

Mind Reader

Put down that crystal ball! You really know your pal well. Try the quiz with another friend and see how well you do.

Do You Mope or Cope?

When things don't go your way, how do you react? Choose the answer that fits you best in each situation, and find out about **your coping style.** Be honest . . .

1. Your grade on the science test was not as good as you had hoped. You're mad at yourself for blowing it and worry about the bad grade for the rest of the day.

   - ☐ That's me.
   - ☐ No way—I would just stick the test in my folder and decide to study more next time.

2. You desperately wanted to win that fluffy stuffed puppy at the carnival, but you just couldn't get it and your whole day is ruined.

   - ☐ That's me.
   - ☐ Not me—I would focus on playing other games and munching on funnel cakes and cotton candy.

3. Your gerbil got loose and you can't find him anywhere. You can't stop blaming yourself for leaving your door open and bury your head in your pillow, worrying about all the bad things that could happen to him.

   - ☐ That's me.
   - ☐ No time for that—I would beg forgiveness and ask my parents to help me find that little guy.

4. You finished your homework just in time to watch your favorite TV show. Only problem? A storm knocked out the power just as the show was about to start. You sit on the couch moaning about what you're missing.

   - ☐ That's me.
   - ☐ No way! I would have fun playing games by candlelight with my family, and I'd catch the show on the reruns.

5. You tried out for the school play but found out today that you didn't make it. You shut yourself in your bedroom and decide that your acting career is over . . . finished . . . kaput!

- ❑ That's me.
- ❑ Not this girl. I might feel sad for a little while, but I would keep practicing hard and try out again next year.

6. You're finishing the cover for your book report. It's getting late, but you really hate the way your drawing looks. You crumple the page and throw the whole thing out. No way can you turn it in like that.

- ❑ That's me.
- ❑ Not quite. I would take a break, have a snack, walk the dog, and then come back to it. It's not THAT bad.

Scoring

4 or more "That's me" answers:

Mope Mode. You tend to let things get you down. Try looking for solutions instead of letting yourself focus on the bad side of things.

3 or fewer "That's me" answers:

Mope? Nope! You like to face a tough situation head on and do something about it. You take things as they come and make the best of whatever happens.

Ways to cope with what gets you down:

- Take a break. Sometimes when you come back to a problem, it doesn't seem nearly as bad as it did when you first discovered it.
- Make a plan. Solving a problem can be less overwhelming when it's broken into smaller tasks.
- Ask for help. Sometimes you need a parent, teacher, or other grown-up to help you solve a particular problem.
- Take a deep breath. Think to yourself, *What's the worst that can happen here?* Chances are, it's not as bad as you first thought. Write down five things that you can do to improve your situation. Then, do them!

Eyewitness

Try this test of your attention to detail. Otis the puppy got into your room. He messed everything up, and now **five things are missing.** Can you tell what they are?

Before Otis

Look at this picture for one minute.

Tick, tick, tick . . . ding! Time's up! Now put the book down and do something else for one minute. Braid your hair, count your freckles—whatever. But make sure you wait at least a minute. Now look at the next page.

After Otis

List what's missing:

1. ______________ 2. ______________ 3. ______________

4. ______________ 5. ______________

Hold this page up to a mirror to see the answers revealed below.

How'd you do?

Scoring

1 or none right	2 or 3 right	4 or 5 right
Clueless	Looking Good	Ace Detective!

Answers: math notebook, teddy bear, baseball cap, bunny slipper, baseball

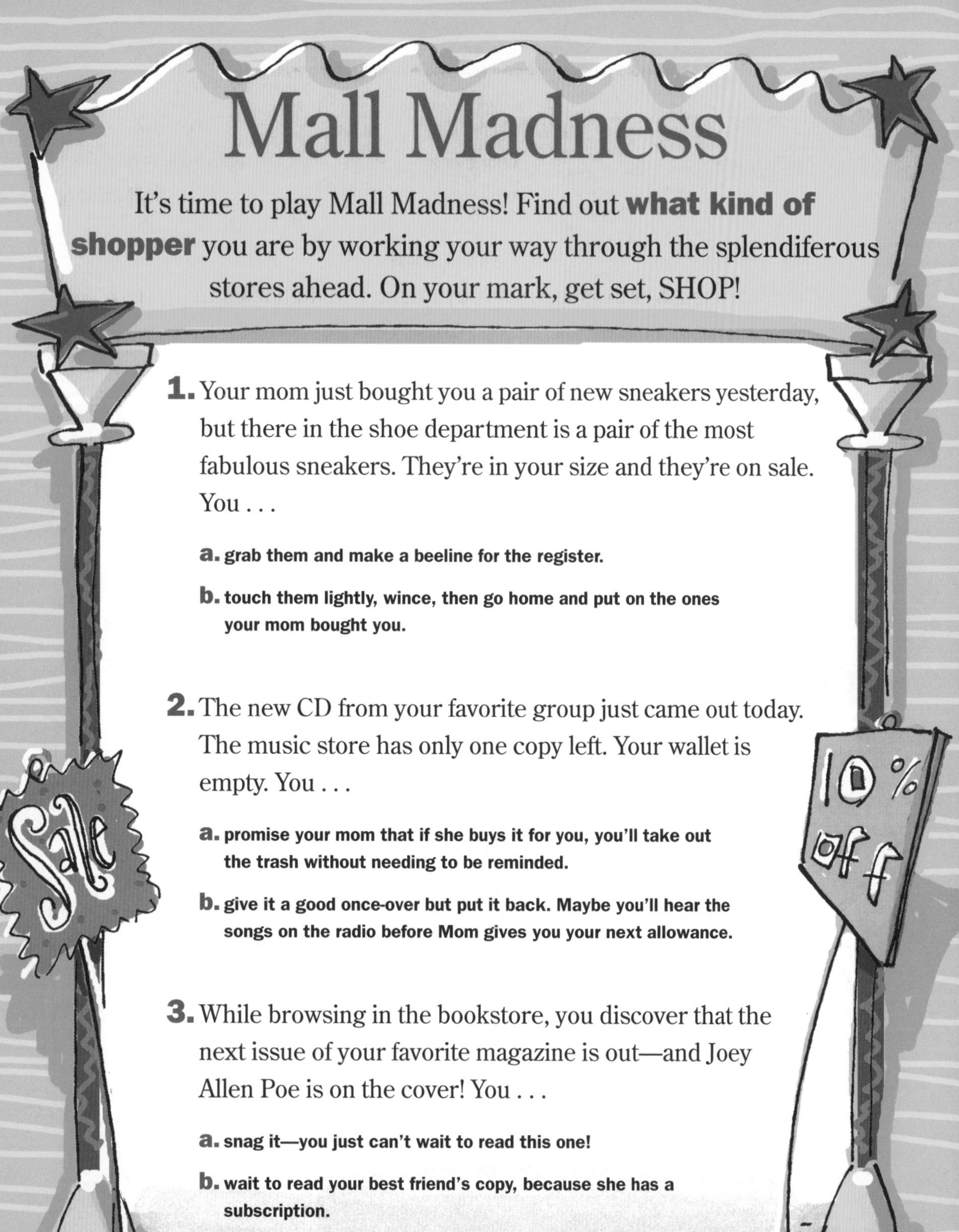

Mall Madness

It's time to play Mall Madness! Find out **what kind of shopper** you are by working your way through the splendiferous stores ahead. On your mark, get set, SHOP!

1. Your mom just bought you a pair of new sneakers yesterday, but there in the shoe department is a pair of the most fabulous sneakers. They're in your size and they're on sale. You . . .

a. **grab them and make a beeline for the register.**

b. **touch them lightly, wince, then go home and put on the ones your mom bought you.**

2. The new CD from your favorite group just came out today. The music store has only one copy left. Your wallet is empty. You . . .

a. **promise your mom that if she buys it for you, you'll take out the trash without needing to be reminded.**

b. **give it a good once-over but put it back. Maybe you'll hear the songs on the radio before Mom gives you your next allowance.**

3. While browsing in the bookstore, you discover that the next issue of your favorite magazine is out—and Joey Allen Poe is on the cover! You . . .

a. **snag it—you just can't wait to read this one!**

b. **wait to read your best friend's copy, because she has a subscription.**

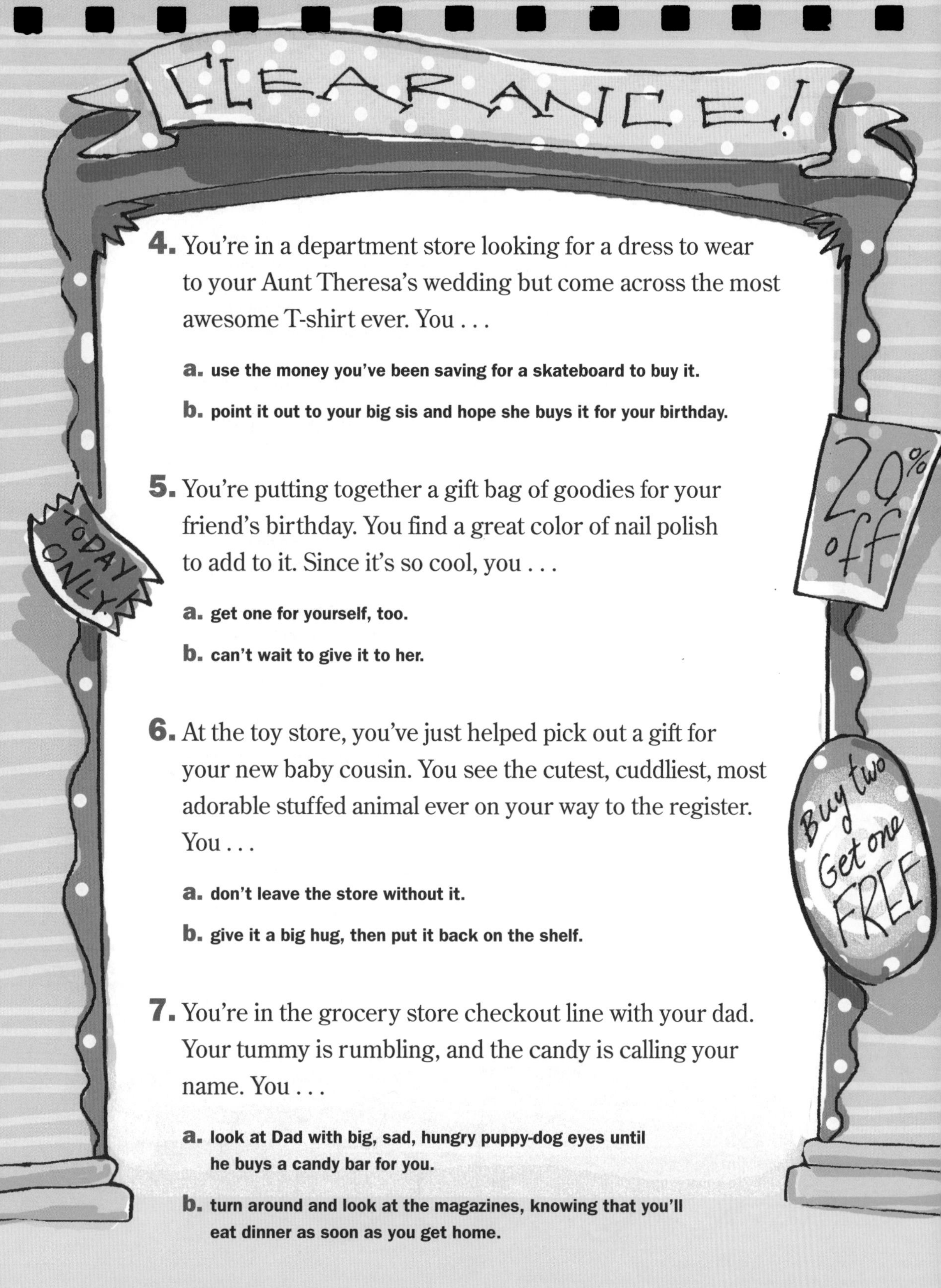

4. You're in a department store looking for a dress to wear to your Aunt Theresa's wedding but come across the most awesome T-shirt ever. You . . .

a. use the money you've been saving for a skateboard to buy it.

b. point it out to your big sis and hope she buys it for your birthday.

5. You're putting together a gift bag of goodies for your friend's birthday. You find a great color of nail polish to add to it. Since it's so cool, you . . .

a. get one for yourself, too.

b. can't wait to give it to her.

6. At the toy store, you've just helped pick out a gift for your new baby cousin. You see the cutest, cuddliest, most adorable stuffed animal ever on your way to the register. You . . .

a. don't leave the store without it.

b. give it a big hug, then put it back on the shelf.

7. You're in the grocery store checkout line with your dad. Your tummy is rumbling, and the candy is calling your name. You . . .

a. look at Dad with big, sad, hungry puppy-dog eyes until he buys a candy bar for you.

b. turn around and look at the magazines, knowing that you'll eat dinner as soon as you get home.

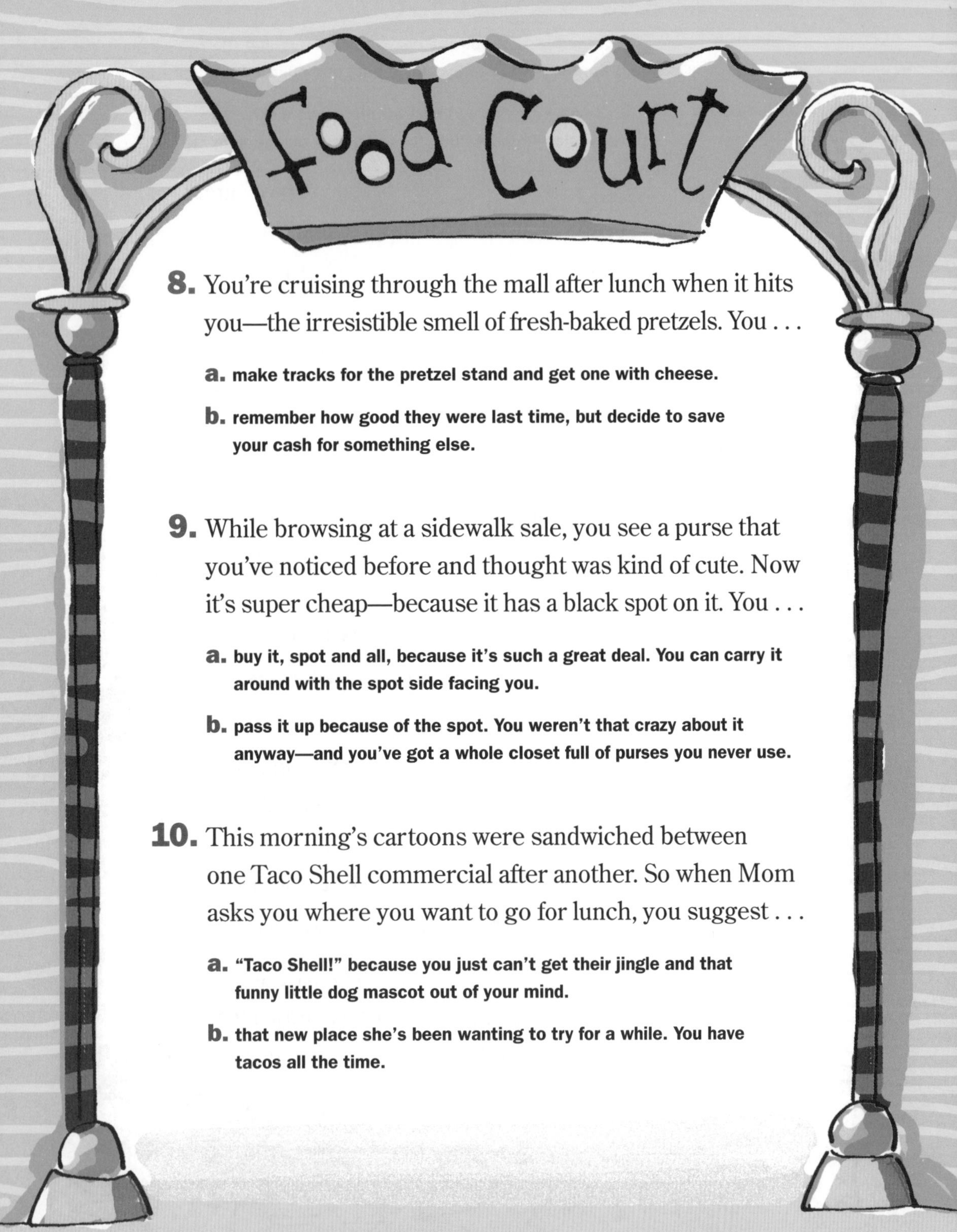

8. You're cruising through the mall after lunch when it hits you—the irresistible smell of fresh-baked pretzels. You . . .

a. **make tracks for the pretzel stand and get one with cheese.**

b. **remember how good they were last time, but decide to save your cash for something else.**

9. While browsing at a sidewalk sale, you see a purse that you've noticed before and thought was kind of cute. Now it's super cheap—because it has a black spot on it. You . . .

a. **buy it, spot and all, because it's such a great deal. You can carry it around with the spot side facing you.**

b. **pass it up because of the spot. You weren't that crazy about it anyway—and you've got a whole closet full of purses you never use.**

10. This morning's cartoons were sandwiched between one Taco Shell commercial after another. So when Mom asks you where you want to go for lunch, you suggest . . .

a. **"Taco Shell!" because you just can't get their jingle and that funny little dog mascot out of your mind.**

b. **that new place she's been wanting to try for a while. You have tacos all the time.**

Answers

Mostly a's

"Gotta Have It" Gal

You love to buy on impulse. It's fun to spend, spend, spend, but sometimes it's better to take a step back and think it over before coughing up the cash. Next time you're about to ring up another sale, ask yourself some questions: "Do I really need this?" "What could I save for instead of buying this?" In other words, "Am I just buying this because of advertising or a super low price?"

Mostly b's

Thoughtful Spender

You're careful with your dough, and you're good at not letting emotions drain your wallet. Kudos to you for taking the time to think about what you want versus what you need—and for not being swayed by ploys used by companies trying to sell things to you.

Happily Ever After?

It's your turn to tell the tale! Choose new endings to these fairy tales and find out **how you like to solve problems.**

1. When the three bears returned home, they should have . . .

a. **called 9-1-1—there was a stranger in the house!**

b. **had a beauty party where they made Goldilocks a redhead.**

2. Cinderella should have . . .

a. **asked the fairy godmother to change the stepsisters into nice people.**

b. **kicked off the glass slippers, ordered a pizza, and invited the prince and the godmother for a late-night snack.**

3. If you wrote the story, Hansel and Gretel would have . . .

a. **brought trail mix and a cell phone along in case they got lost.**

b. **turned the witch into a gingerbread cookie and eaten her!**

4. Snow White would have been better off if she . . .

a. **had tossed the poison apple and kept on cleaning house.**

b. **had gone on tour singing "Heigh-ho, Heigh-ho, It's Home from Work We Go," with the dwarves as backup and the prince as her manager.**

5. "Little Red Riding Hood" should have ended with . . .

a. **Red Riding Hood convincing the wolf to cut it out and have some tea and muffins with her and Grandmother.**

b. **Red Riding Hood overpowering the wolf. Those Tae Kwon Do lessons paid off!**

6. "The Three Little Pigs" would have been a better story if . . .

a. **the three little pigs had convinced the wolf to become a vegetarian.**

b. **the pigs' houses had secret underground tunnels through which they escaped to a space shuttle that took them to their REAL home on the moon.**

7. "Jack and the Beanstalk" should have ended with . . .

a. **Jack and the giant agreeing to share the goose.**

b. **Jack and his mother opening the Beanstalk Amusement Park, featuring the Golden Goose Log Flume, the Tickle-the-Giant Sideshow, and the Magic Beans Super Slide.**

8. Rapunzel should have . . .

a. **offered to make the witch a wig out of some of her hair in exchange for being set free.**

b. **parachuted out of the tower and gone straight to the hairstylist for a snazzy new 'do.**

Answers

Mostly a's

A Lot o' Logic

You use logic and rational problem solving to get yourself out of jams (and to keep from getting into them!). You think before you act, always have a plan, and need to know the reason behind something before buying into it.

Mostly b's

A Bit o' Whimsy

You have quite an imagination! You're creative and fun in your problem solving. You always look for new, different answers. You like to see happy endings, but you're also up for exciting twists and turns along the way.

Raise Your Hand

Some people believe that **palm reading,** or looking at the lines on your hands, can tell you about your personality. Look at your palms and the information on the next page and see if you agree!

Head Line

Your head line tells what kind of thinker you are. If it's straight, you are logical and interested in facts. If it curves down a bit, you are good at math and science. If it curves down a lot, you're very creative and imaginative.

Heart Line

Your heart line tells about your feelings. The stronger the heart line, the more affectionate and caring you may be. If it slants up, you are a true, warmhearted friend. If it's straight, your head rules your heart.

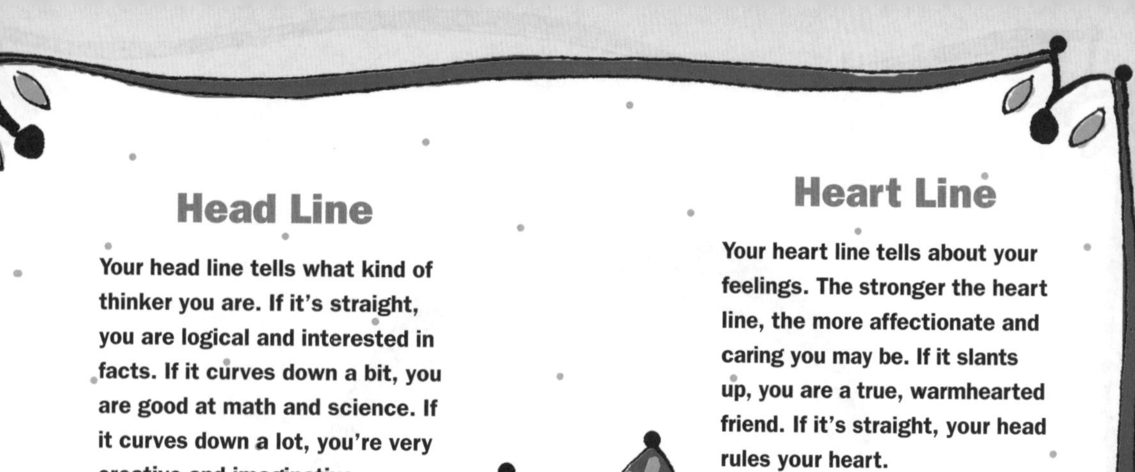

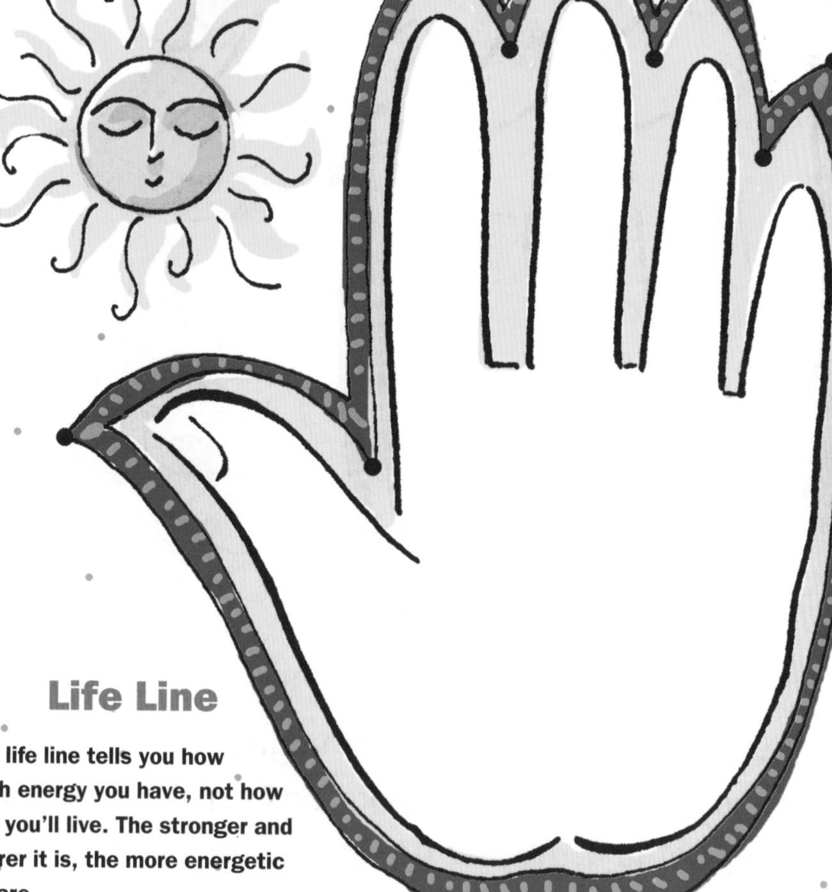

Use the guide on page 33 and draw your lines here.

Life Line

Your life line tells you how much energy you have, not how long you'll live. The stronger and clearer it is, the more energetic you are.

Back in the Day

What were your parents like at your age? What did they consider cool, neat, or cute? Write the answers to the following questions with one parent in mind. Then have Mom or Dad check your answers to find out how much you know.

1. Street he or she grew up on ....

2. Pet's name ....

3. Best friend's name ....

4. Favorite relative ....

5. Name of school attended ....

6. Best school subject ....

7. Favorite hangout ....

8. Dream job ....

9. Subject of posters on bedroom wall ....

10. Best gift ever ....

11. Favorite book ....

12. Favorite Halloween costume ....

13. Favorite toy or belonging ....

14. Favorite TV show ....

15. Number of televisions in the house ....

16. Favorite movie star ....

17. Favorite band or singer ....

18. Kept a collection of ....

19. Favorite board game ....

20. Favorite sport ....

21. Favorite team ....

22. Favorite drink ....

23. Favorite fast food ....

24. Favorite sweet treat ....

25. Least favorite veggie ....

26. Favorite holiday ....

27. Family vacation spot ....

28. Price of a school lunch ....

29. Amount of allowance ....

30. President of the United States ....

Scoring

Give yourself 1 point for each correct answer.

0 to 9 points

Things were really different when your parent was a kid! There's so much to learn about life back then and about what your parent was like. Go through the quiz together and learn more!

10 to 19 points

Although you know quite a bit about what your parent did as a kid, there's more to learn and probably quite a few funny stories you haven't heard. Have your parent tell you the answers you missed!

20 to 30 points

Wow! You must have listened carefully to those "When I was your age . . ." stories. You know a lot about your parent's life as a kid. Try taking the quiz with another parent or relative in mind.

Doyouknowthis.com

Are you up on the latest **Internet I.M. lingo?** Log on to this quiz, enter your answers in the blanks, then scroll to the next page to check them.

1. :-Z ___
2. PAW ___
3. GAL ___
4. J/K ___
5. *<:-) ___
6. SYL ___
7. 8-P ___
8. ABM ___
9. IK ___
10. (()):** ___
11. BCNU ___
12. :-# ___
13. DYJHIW ___
14. :-x ___
15. CWS ___
16. %-(___
17. GMTA ___
18. :D ___

a. Just kidding
b. Santa Claus
c. Parents are watching
d. Cool Web stuff
e. I know
f. See ya later
g. Get a life
h. Be seeing you
i. Yuck
j. Sleeping
k. Great minds think alike
l. A big mistake
m. Confused
n. Don't you just hate it when
o. Hugs and kisses
p. Keeping lips sealed
q. Someone with braces
r. Laughing

Answers

1. j. Sleeping **2.** c. Parents are watching **3.** g. Get a life **4.** a. Just kidding **5.** b. Santa Claus **6.** f. See ya later **7.** i. Yuck **8.** l. A big mistake **9.** e. I know **10.** o. Hugs and kisses **11.** h. Be seeing you **12.** q. Someone with braces **13.** n. Don't you just hate it when **14.** p. Keeping lips sealed **15.** d. Cool Web stuff **16.** m. Confused **17.** k. Great minds think alike **18.** r. Laughing

Scoring

Give yourself 1 point for each correct answer.

0 to 6 points

In Training

Need a little practice in e-conversations? Give a few of these abbreviations and emoticons a try. (If you don't have a computer at home, test-drive one at your local library.)

7 to 12 points

With It

You're pretty hip when it comes to knowing Internet talk. Try making up more codes of your own!

13 to 18 points

It Clicked!

You're a computer queen. You've probably even made up a few of your own abbreviations and emoticons!

What Kind of Friend Are You?

Are you the **first one to give a hug, always ready to rescue,** or **not so sure** where you stand? Take this quiz to find out!

1. Your friend Neeta is thinking about signing up for the science-fair competition at school. You . . .

- ❑ **tell Neeta that it's a great idea! Then tell her you can do the project together and start sketching your plans.**
- ❑ **wonder if you should sign up, too. You don't want to miss anything . . . but you aren't really sure either.**
- ❑ **are so excited for her, you make plans to attend and show your support.**

2. Yikes! Your teacher surprised everyone with a pop quiz in social studies today. Afterward, you say to your friends . . .

- ❑ **"No one was really prepared, but I bet we all did O.K." Then you put your arms around them and make a run for the monkey bars.**
- ❑ **"How many do you think you got wrong?"**
- ❑ **"Let's study together this weekend so we're prepared next time."**

3. Kristen is wearing a new fuzzy sweater that everyone totally loves. Your reaction is to . . .

- ❑ tell her how great it looks on her.
- ❑ zip your coat so no one looks next at the plain old sweatshirt you're wearing.
- ❑ ask her where she got it and have your mom buy you the exact same one.

4. Your soccer team makes it to the finals but loses in the last minute of the game. After the game, you . . .

- ❑ congratulate your teammates on a terrific season and remind them that there's always next year.
- ❑ tell everyone that you're going to organize an off-season conditioning program.
- ❑ worry that your teammates think it was your fault you lost—you should have made that goal you missed.

5. Valerie tells you her parents are getting divorced and she has to move away. You . . .

- ❑ tell her you're sorry and you'll always be her friend whenever she needs to talk.
- ❑ worry that you'll never make another friend.
- ❑ start planning a going-away party and think of ways you can e-mail and visit each other.

6. Jen comes to school on crutches after she sprained her ankle. You . . .

- ❑ secretly wish you were the one on crutches so that you could get all the attention.
- ❑ ask her how it happened and tell her how sorry you are that she got hurt.
- ❑ carry her books for her and put your sweatshirt under her foot to elevate it.

7. Lily has been your best friend since first grade, but lately she doesn't sit next to you during lunch and seems to want to hang out only with Laura. You . . .

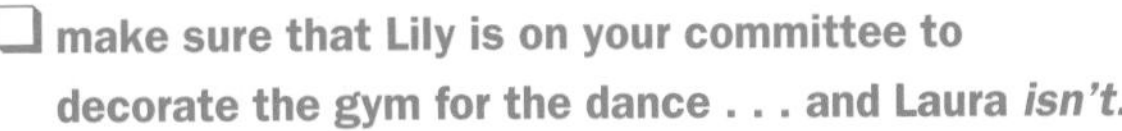

- ❑ make sure that Lily is on your committee to decorate the gym for the dance . . . and Laura *isn't.*
- ❑ sneak a note into her locker telling her that you miss her.
- ❑ can't help but wonder why she doesn't like you anymore.

8. It's the last day of school! The last thing you do at school is . . .

- ❑ give all your friends big hugs.
- ❑ peek over your friends' shoulders as they open their report cards.
- ❑ make sure all your friends have each others' camp addresses for care packages!

Answers

mostly blue

You are always ready to lend an ear and offer words of encouragement to your friends. You know yourself and you know how to be a good friend at the same time. Your friends can count on you.

mostly red

You are creative—a natural leader! You like to plan, coordinate, and help out. But you need to be careful not to take too much control, especially when no one asks you to. Be patient, listen, and try not to always jump to the rescue! You might find some ways to put your leadership skills to use, like heading up the school food drive.

mostly yellow

You sometimes feel insecure about yourself. Try to remember that you, too, have special strengths, and don't put so much emphasis on how you measure up to your pals.

Boy Barometer

Are boys your **new hobby, just O.K.,** or **pretty icky?** Check the barometer and see what your reading is.

1. You have new assigned seats in math class, and you're stuck between two boys. You . . .

a. **don't know how you will live through it.**

b. **don't really mind because they are nice enough guys.**

c. **think it's pretty cool.**

2. Your friend Jade likes Dominic, and she won't stop talking about him. You . . .

a. **think she's nuts.**

b. **aren't sure why she wants to gush but are O.K. listening to the details . . . for a little while.**

c. **ask Jade if Dominic has any friends.**

3. You sign up for a summer class in archery but find out you're the only girl in the class. You . . .

a. **drop out and take swimming instead.**

b. **go because you really want to do this.**

c. **can hardly wait—being the only girl will be so cool!**

4. Your gym teacher announces that the boys and girls will be together outside today for track. Your first thought is . . .

a. **"My stomach hurts. I'm going to the nurse's office."**

b. **"I love the long jump."**

c. **"I'm going to need extra time to look just right for this."**

5. You're invited to your friend Kevin's birthday party. The first thing you do is . . .

a. **throw out the invitation. You don't want people to think you like him.**

b. **call to RSVP. He's a friend, so of course you'll go.**

c. **call your friends to tell them you're going to a girl-boy birthday party.**

6. Jay is the only person your age at the family holiday party for your mom's office. You . . .

a. **ignore him and go help out at the beanbag toss for the little kids.**

b. **roll your eyes at him when someone suggests you dance together.**

c. **trade seats with someone so that you end up sitting next to him for the dinner.**

7. You're staying at your aunt's house. You're looking for a book to read, but all you find are your cousin's teen fan magazines. You . . .

a. **forget about reading and go see if she has cable.**

b. **read a little of one that has your favorite actor on the front.**

c. **stack them up and plan to read every single one before you leave.**

8. Student Council has planned an end-of-year dance for your grade. You . . .

a. **would rather invite some friends over to play board games at your house that night.**

b. **plan to go, but only if you and your best bud can go together.**

c. **hope that the cute guy who just moved here will ask you to go with him.**

Scoring

Give yourself 0 points for each a, 1 point for each b, and 2 points for each c. Color in one of the sections on the barometer for each point.

0 to 4
No Thanks

Chances are you have better things to do than worry about boys. It is perfectly fine not to be gaga over guys. Go with what makes you feel comfortable.

5 to 9
Boy Friends?

For you, boys don't have to be "boyfriends." You are able to get to know boys for who they are and even enjoy being friends with some of them.

10 to 16
Oh Boy!

It's nice to be friendly and even curious about boys, but ask yourself if your new hobby is taking over your life. Boys are just . . . boys. Keep your other interests alive, too.

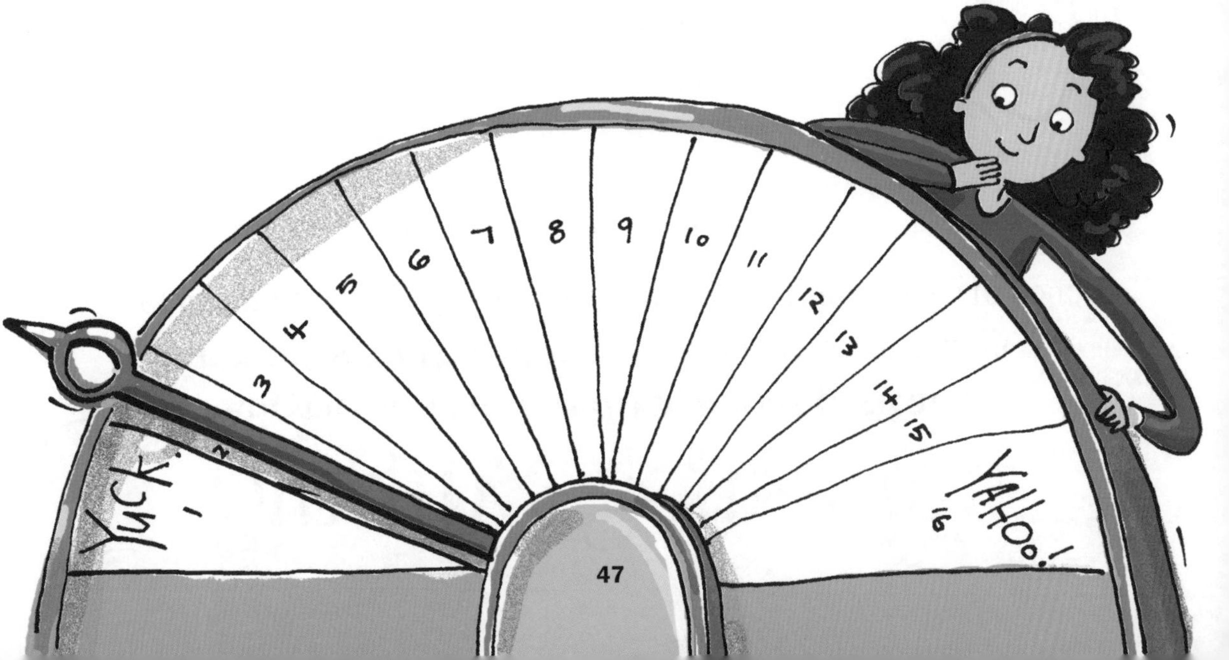

Singing Sensation

Are you cut out to be **a diva, a songwriter,** or **a manager to the stars?** Find out where you fit in the entertainment biz. Check each statement that applies to you.

_____ **I love being in front of a crowd.**

_____ **I'm very good at organizing.**

_____ **I always have lots of exciting new ideas.**

_____ **I'm happiest when I'm alone.**

_____ **People look to me to make decisions.**

_____ **I adore flashy new fashions.**

_____ **I sometimes exaggerate.**

_____ **I like to plan things out.**

_____ **I keep a journal or sketchbook.**

_____ **I adore it when people pay attention to me.**

_____ **I like to be near excitement but not right in the middle of it.**

_____ I am usually pretty quiet, but there's a lot going on inside my head.

_____ I am proud of my abilities, and I am not afraid to stand up and show the world what I can do.

_____ Music, art, and poetry make life worthwhile.

_____ I try not to get caught up in silly things and try to keep myself focused.

Answers

Mostly red

Delightful Diva

You love to be the star of the show and would be at home at center stage.

Mostly blue

Management Material

You love to organize and be a leader. You would do a great job steering a star's career.

Mostly green

Certainly a Songwriter

You tend to be creative and are happiest when you can give your free spirit room to play.

Read Between the Lines

What kind of books get you hooked?
Check out this quiz and find your **book style.**

1. You and a pal decide to go see a movie. You've just got to see the one called . . .

   a. ***Spy Twins.***

   b. ***Behind the Velvet Curtains: Secrets of Teenage Royalty.***

   c. ***Pandas in China: A Rescue Mission.***

2. You're in the grocery checkout line with your dad. Which headline catches your eye?

   a. **"Aliens Have Arrived" on the front page of the *American Inquirer***

   b. **"101 Great Ideas for Girls' Bedrooms" in *Beautiful Home***

   c. **"Kids Care: Volunteer Opportunities for Kids" in the *Everyday News***

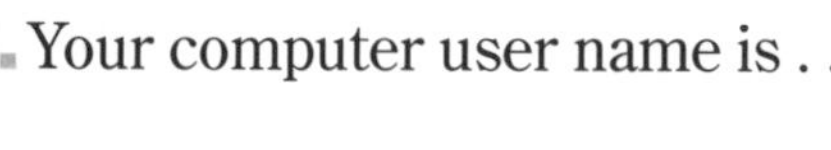

3. Your computer user name is . . .

   a. **a secret.**

   b. **Dreamer.**

   c. **Down-2-Earth.**

4. You're shipwrecked on a desert island. You plan to . . .

a. learn to spearfish and track the large paw prints you've seen in the sand.

b. use coconuts and shells to create a rocket that will hone in on the nearest aircraft carrier and alert the crew to your location.

c. keep a daily journal—once you're rescued, you'll sell your life story.

5. Your favorite board game is . . .

a. Clue.

b. The Game of Life.

c. Trivial Pursuit.

6. When you were little, you liked to play . . .

a. Hide-and-Seek.

b. Dress-Up.

c. House.

7. The creatures that interest you the most are . . .

a. the Loch Ness Monster and Bigfoot.

b. unicorns and trolls.

c. dogs and horses.

8. It's time to plan your family's summer vacation. You suggest . . .

a. a Secret Escape—a travel agent makes all the arrangements, and nobody knows where you're headed until a few days before the trip.

b. a Caribbean cruise—just like in the movies!

c. a family reunion—what a perfect way to meet all your cousins.

9. On your birthday, the gift you want to open first is . . .

a. the giant box that makes a strange noise when you shake it.

b. the one wrapped in shiny gold paper with lots of cascading curlicue ribbons.

c. the one shaped like the camera you've been wanting.

Answers:

5 or more **a's**
Mystery Maven:
It's no mystery that you love suspense, intrigue, and finding out secrets. You would probably really enjoy adventure or mystery stories.

5 or more **b's**
Flights of Fancy:
You love to learn about magical people and places and to pretend you're lost in other worlds. Chances are, fantasy books would strike your fancy.

5 or more **c's**
Just the Facts, Ma'am:
The truth is, you're intrigued by real-life situations and real people's problems. You should try reading nonfiction or realistic fiction.

A mix of **a's, b's,** and **c's**
Story Smorgasbord:
You have lots of different tastes and interests, so you could choose from a variety of different books—from fact to fiction!

Stress Test

Being involved can be a good thing, but being overcommitted can be a disaster! **Hook yourself up to the stress monitor** to see if your extracurricular schedule is balanced . . . or off the charts!

1. When you first wake up in the morning, you . . .

a. **wish you could stay in bed.**

b. **worry that you don't have everything done.**

c. **are excited and ready to start the day.**

2. Lately, you find yourself getting annoyed with your friends and family . . .

a. **all the time.**

b. **once in a while.**

c. **almost never.**

3. You have something scheduled after school . . .

a. **every day.**

b. **most days.**

c. **once in a while.**

4. You find yourself crying or getting upset . . .

a. every couple of days.

b. every couple of weeks.

c. hardly ever.

5. It's hard for you to find time to do things like clean your room, paint your nails, or read a book . . .

a. often.

b. sometimes.

c. almost never.

6. You find yourself wishing there were more hours in the day . . .

a. all the time.

b. once a week.

c. once a month.

7. You wake up in the night worrying . . .

a. a couple times a week.

b. a few times a month.

c. hardly ever.

8. On the weekends, you have time to sleep in, hang out with your family, or do something just for you . . .

a. **once a month.**

b. **every couple of weeks.**

c. **every weekend.**

Scoring

Give yourself 3 points for each a, 2 points for each b, and 1 point for each c.

19 to 24: Stress Mess: **You have so much going on in your life right now that it's time for a time-out. Take a moment and think about what's really important to you. Something *has* to go!**

14 to 18: Happily Challenged: **It's great to be busy. But remember that too much of a good thing can become a bad thing. Keep an eye on your schedule and make sure you don't overdo it.**

8 to 13: Stressless: **You're pretty comfortable with your schedule. You might take time to try out new activities that interest you. But don't feel like you have to be busy to be happy.**

Best Buds?

Did you know that when you give someone a bouquet, you're really sending a secret message? **Test your flower power** by matching these blooms with their meanings.

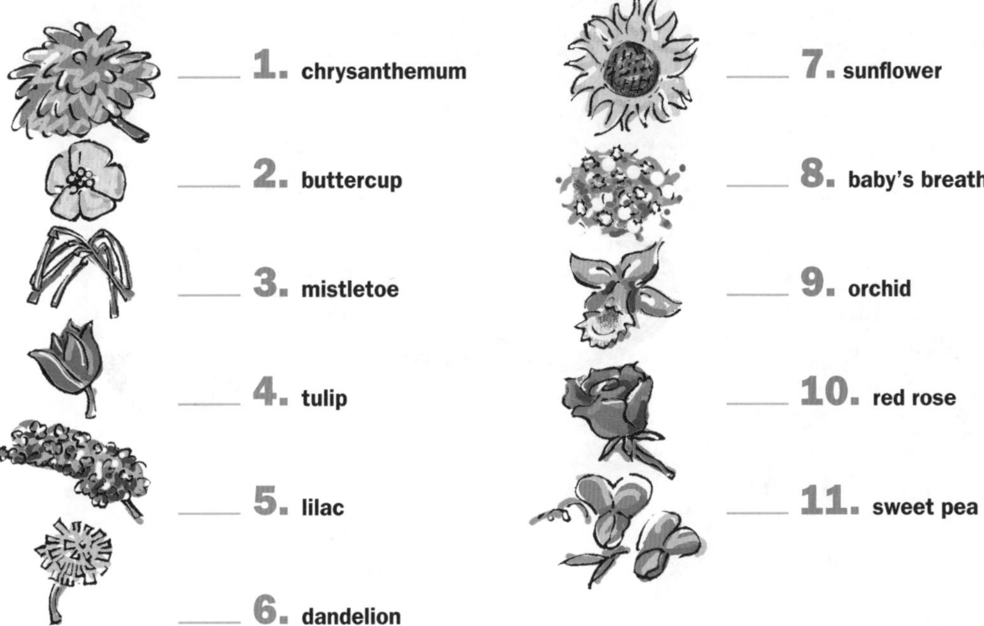

____ **1.** chrysanthemum

____ **2.** buttercup

____ **3.** mistletoe

____ **4.** tulip

____ **5.** lilac

____ **6.** dandelion

____ **7.** sunflower

____ **8.** baby's breath

____ **9.** orchid

____ **10.** red rose

____ **11.** sweet pea

a. You're so sweet.

b. See you later!

c. I promise.

d. You're a wonderful friend.

e. You're silly.

f. I believe in you.

g. You're beautiful.

h. Give me a smooch!

i. I love you.

j. You're famous!

k. Great job!

Answers

1. d. You're a wonderful friend. **2.** e. You're silly. **3.** h. Give me a smooch! **4.** j. You're famous!

5. f. I believe in you. **6.** c. I promise. **7.** k. Great job! **8.** a. You're so sweet.

9. g. You're beautiful. **10.** i. I love you. **11.** b. See you later!

Scoring

0 to 3 correct

Nipped in the Bud

Don't worry if you didn't know these. Now that you've learned how to send secret messages with flowers, have fun!

4 to 7 correct

Just Blossoming

You knew a lot of these! To learn even more, look for a book at your library!

8 to 11 correct

Blooming Genius

Nice going! You have true petal power.

Try sending messages to your friends using drawings of some of these flowers as codes.

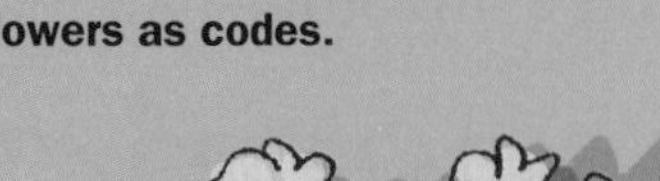

What's Your Recipe for Making Friends?

When it comes to **making new friends,** do you bubble over with enthusiasm, or are you a bit slow to warm up?

1. You're vacationing at a beach cottage. Next door are two girls about your age. You . . .

a. run over and invite them to go swimming with you.

b. watch them for a while to see if they look nice before introducing yourself.

c. read your magazine outside and hope they see you and say hi.

2. A new girl has just started at your school. You . . .

a. ask her to sit with you at lunch.

b. smile when she sits next to you and tell her your name.

c. avoid her until you find out what she's like.

3. Your best pal, Beth, invites you to come to her house for a sleepover with her cousins. You . . .

a. can't wait to go. If the cousins are anything like Beth, you know you'll have a great time.

b. ask her a little bit about the cousins before deciding if you'll go.

c. tell her you're busy that night—you just know you'd feel weird spending the night with a bunch of girls you've never met.

4. Your family just moved, and you're going to your first day at the new school. The bus pulls up to your stop. You . . .

a. hop on and walk straight to the back, where all the action is.

b. cautiously find a seat in the middle with a girl who looks about your age.

c. sit in the first available seat—right behind the bus driver.

5. You're sitting in the bleachers at your brother's soccer game. Two girls are sitting next to you. You . . .

a. say, "Who wants to go get a hot dog?" to see if they'll join you.

b. ask them who they're there to watch.

c. listen in on their conversation to figure out if they're nice.

6. You're browsing through your favorite store at the mall while your mom is trying on shoes. The girl flipping through the rack next to you looks familiar. You . . .

a. say hi and ask if you know her.

b. smile and see if she smiles back.

c. keep shopping and see if she notices you.

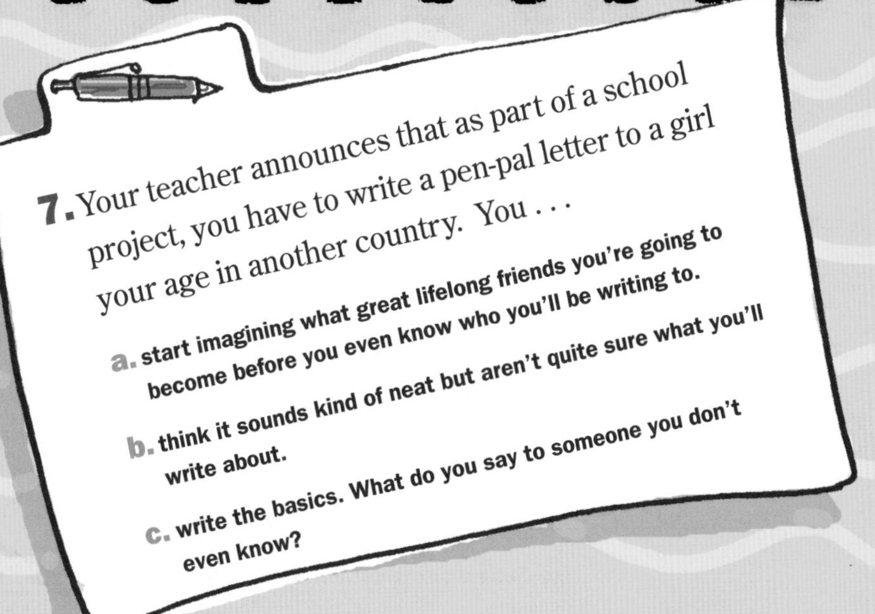

7. Your teacher announces that as part of a school project, you have to write a pen-pal letter to a girl your age in another country. You . . .

a. start imagining what great lifelong friends you're going to become before you even know who you'll be writing to.

b. think it sounds kind of neat but aren't quite sure what you'll write about.

c. write the basics. What do you say to someone you don't even know?

Scoring

Give yourself 1 point for each c, 2 points for each b, and 3 points for each a.

7 to 11

Slow Cooker: You tend to make friends slowly, which can make for strong and steady friendships. But be sure you're not letting great friendships slip through the cracks. All relationships involve a little risk—don't be afraid to take one if it means meeting a new pal.

12 to 16

Simmering: You're open to new people but are also cautious. Once you feel comfortable, you're not afraid to take the initiative to meet new friends or to let people get to know you.

17 to 21

Hot! Hot! Hot!: You're totally comfortable in new environments. With you and friends, the more the merrier! Make sure, though, that you're taking the time to nurture and grow the friendships you have.

Birds of a Feather

If you were a bird, what kind would you be? Choose the answers that describe you best and find out which **feathered friend** fits you.

1. When you get older, you would love a job as . . .

a. **Princess Odette in *Swan Lake* with the national tour of a ballet company.**

b. **the *Quiz Book* editor.**

c. **a Peace Corps volunteer teaching children in another country.**

d. **a cover model for *American Woman* magazine.**

e. **the star of a hilarious new television series.**

f. **an award-winning roving photojournalist.**

2. Your perfect day would be . . .

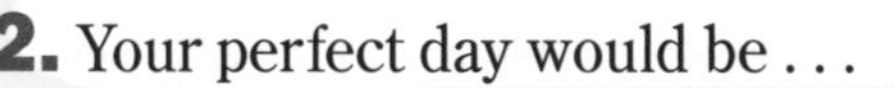

a. **shopping for antiques with your older sisters.**

b. **sleeping till after noon and staying up half the night reading a novel.**

c. **playing board games with your family in front of the fireplace.**

d. **shopping for new clothes at the mega-mall.**

e. **painting your bedroom fuschia and lime.**

f. **hunting for seashells on the beach.**

3. Your favorite shirt, blouse, or sweater is . . .

a. **elegant and lacy.**

b. **dark and serious.**

c. **soft and comfortable.**

d. **decorated with glitter and rhinestones.**

e. **bright and colorful.**

f. **plain and simple.**

4. On your dream vacation, you would most want to stay . . .

a. at a beautiful country inn with fluffy canopy beds.

b. right in the middle of a big city, within walking distance of museums and a huge art gallery.

c. at your family's lake cottage—where you can relax on the dock.

d. at a posh resort with poolside waiters, spa service, and a concierge to plan your day.

e. on a tropical island—basking in the warm sun and frolicking in the soft white sand.

f. at a campground in the wild west, horseback riding by day, and roasting marshmallows and singing around a campfire by night.

5. You most love to shop at . . .

a. La Boutique, an expensive designer shop.

b. A-Million-&-One Books bookstore.

c. Hometowne Mall, where you can find everything you want under one roof.

d. Glamour Girls jewelry and accessories store.

e. The Buck $top dollar shop, where you can find lots of cool cheap stuff.

f. Good Sports sporting goods store.

6. The scent that you like the most is . . .

a. a bundle of freshly picked lilacs.

b. a brand-new book, especially if it's the newest release from your favorite author.

c. Dad's delicioso dinner cooking.

d. your freshly shampooed hair.

e. Mom's brand-new car.

f. the air outside after a spring rain shower.

Answers

Mostly a's: You're like a swan and love graceful, elegant things.

Mostly b's: Like the wise owl, you are a night person and love knowledge.

Mostly c's: You're kind and caring and resemble the dove, the symbol of peace.

Mostly d's: Like the peacock, you adore making a big splash.

Mostly e's: Quirky and bright, you resemble the parrot.

Mostly f's: Like the eagle, you love freedom and to soar in the great outdoors!

Grudge Meter

When you feel that you've been wronged, do you **hold a grudge** or can you **forgive and forget?**

1. Last year Alana didn't invite you to her birthday party. You're making up the guest list for your birthday bash, and you . . .

a. put her on the list since she's still part of your group.

b. put her down with a question mark since you're not sure what to do.

c. definitely do not invite her. If you weren't welcome at her party, she's not coming to yours.

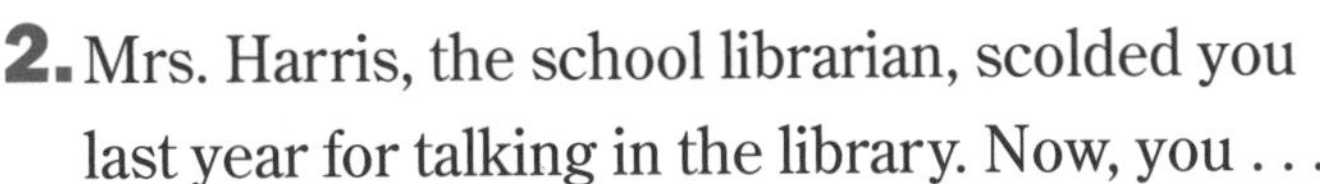

2. Mrs. Harris, the school librarian, scolded you last year for talking in the library. Now, you . . .

a. show her how you've matured by smiling and zipping your lips whenever you see her.

b. avoid the library at all costs—or try to go during Mrs. Harris's lunch period.

c. call Mrs. Harris "Mrs. Scare-us" (behind her back, of course).

3. When you were little, your Uncle Mel used to call you Chubby Cheeks. Whenever you see him now, you . . .

a. smile and tell him about your last basketball game. You're not Chubby Cheeks anymore!

b. try to be polite. You still remember what he used to say, but you know he was just trying to be funny.

c. roll your eyes and leave the room. You have nothing to say to him.

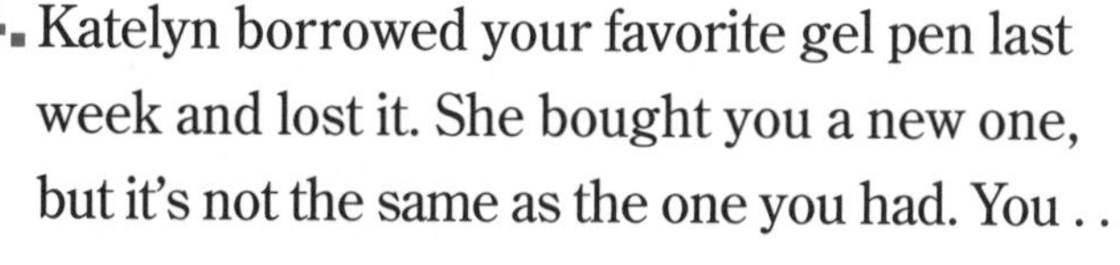

4. Katelyn borrowed your favorite gel pen last week and lost it. She bought you a new one, but it's not the same as the one you had. You . . .

a. tell her it's O.K. A gel pen is a gel pen. It's not like she meant to lose it.

b. say "thanks," but make the decision to keep the lending to a minimum for a while.

c. find yourself thinking about it every time you use the pen, and end up treating Katelyn differently afterward.

5. At your softball game, you and Mariah collide as you both try to make the game-winning catch, and the ball drops to the ground between you. You have another game the next day. You . . .

a. try to concentrate on getting ready for the game. What happened was yesterday's news.

b. talk to Mariah about you both remembering to yell "I got it!" before making a catch.

c. avoid Mariah, vow not to throw the ball to her, and whisper to your friends that you think she's a show-off.

6. The last time you painted your little sister's toenails, she accidentally spilled the bottle of nail polish all over your bedroom floor. Now she wants you to paint her nails again. You . . .

a. go ahead and do it. She didn't mean to make a mess the last time.

b. remember to put down newspaper this time and remind her to be careful.

c. tell her "No way!" You don't want her making another mess in your room.

7. Your kitten claws your favorite teddy bear to shreds. You . . .

a. sigh and clean up the mess. He's just a kitten and you love him.

b. put your other valuables away, then go on the Internet and get some information on kitten training.

c. yell "Get outta here!" every time he comes into your room.

8. While cleaning out your closet, you find a mean note from Jennie to Chelsea about you that you intercepted last year. You . . .

a. toss it without reading it again. You're all friends now, so who cares?

b. try to think about what the fight was really about, then write in your journal about your newfound insights.

c. save it, and don't speak to Jennie the next day at school.

Scoring

Score 1 point for each a, 2 points for each b, and 3 points for each c.

8 to 12:
Easy Come, Easy Go

You let go of problems easily and leave the past behind you. Just be careful not to let people take advantage of your good nature.

13 to 18:
Future Focused

You're pretty good at forgiving and forgetting, but you also want to prevent bad situations from happening again. You realize that you can't change the past, so you try to look to the future.

19 to 24:
Grudge Master

You have the memory of an elephant, but you can't let go of the times when you've been hurt. Ask yourself: *Did these people mean to hurt me?* Most of the time, the answer is no. When you hold a grudge, you're really hurting yourself. You'll feel better if you can let go of some of the anger you're holding.

The Scoop

Did you know that some people say your **favorite ice cream flavor** shows a lot about your personality? Circle your favorite flavor, then turn the page to see what it says about you.

Vanilla	Chocolate Chip
Double Chocolate Chunk	Strawberries and Cream
Banana Split	Butter Pecan

Answers

Vanilla: You're not just plain vanilla. You are always busy and have lots of friends. You expect an awful lot from yourself, though, so remember that it's O.K. to stop and taste the ice cream once in a while.

Strawberries and Cream: You're a bit on the shy side but comfortable exploring the world on your own. You like friends who look on the bright side of things.

Banana Split: You're easy to get along with and a good listener. You take most things in stride and don't let the little things get you down.

Chocolate Chip: You are always looking to the future, and wow, do you have great plans for yourself! You love to compete but aren't so happy when you lose.

Butter Pecan: You have your life all planned and organized. You tend to keep your feelings to yourself and go it alone.

Double Chocolate Chunk: You love to have fun and adore being the center of attention. You tend to trust other people and are always looking for friends. You follow your hunches.

Mighty Manners?

There's more to manners than "please" and "thank you."
See if you know what to do in these situations.

1. You call Allie to invite her over for dinner, but no one answers. Instead, you get her family's answering machine. You . . .

a. **hang up. You hate those machines.**

b. **say, "Phone tag. You're it! Call me!" She'll know it's you.**

c. **leave a message: "This is Jamie. Can Allie please call me back this afternoon?"**

2. Mom is psyched to serve her new soup recipe when proper Aunt Emily comes over for dinner. You smile politely as you lift your soup spoon, then impress the adults by remembering to . . .

a. **daintily scoop the soup toward yourself (that's the proper way to eat soup, you know).**

b. **blow lightly on each spoonful before you eat it.**

c. **tilt your bowl to spoon up the last scrumptious drop!**

3. Sweet peas are your favorite green veggie. But those babies can be hard to catch! To eat them, you should . . .

a. push a few peas onto your fork with your finger when nobody's looking.

b. carefully use your knife to corral the peas onto your fork.

c. quickly stab the peas with your fork.

4. After the group belts out the final notes of "Happy Birthday" at your friend's party, it's the moment you've been waiting for . . . the cake. But—wait—is that CARROT cake? Gross! Now what?

a. Take a small slice and give it a try. Maybe at least the frosting is yummy.

b. Announce to the group that you don't do veggies in your desserts, "No, thank you!"

c. Politely ask your friend's mom for a different kind of cake.

5. Oops! You drop your napkin way under the table at a restaurant and can't even reach it with your foot. You should . . .

a. crawl under the table and get it.

b. use your brother's.

c. ask for a new one.

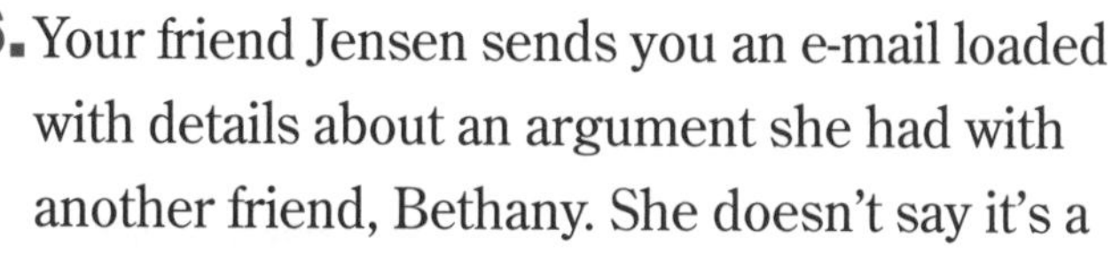

6. Your friend Jensen sends you an e-mail loaded with details about an argument she had with another friend, Bethany. She doesn't say it's a secret, so you . . .

a. **forward the message to a few other friends. Everyone has been having trouble with Bethany lately—this is so typical!**

b. **respond to Jensen but try to change the subject. Who knows where the message might end up?**

c. **respond to Jensen, but include Bethany in the reply (so that she gets a copy of Jensen's original message). She can't change unless she knows there's a problem.**

7. Your stomach is growling and your usual dinnertime was an hour ago, but there's no sign of food yet at the party you're at. You . . .

a. **look around and ask loudly, "So, when ARE we eating?"**

b. **sneak out to the kitchen and try to sneak a snack.**

c. **ask your friend to ask her mom for a little something to tide you over.**

8. After your soccer game, the team heads to the Pizza Pit for the all-you-can-eat buffet. You're so hungry, you're ready for seconds before anyone else. When you go back to the buffet for another slice, you . . .

a. **bring your plate with you. The dishwasher will appreciate having fewer dishes to wash.**

b. **leave your plate at the table. Just walk up to the buffet and get a slice—it's finger food!**

c. **start with a clean plate each time you return to the buffet. Who wants to use a dirty dish?**

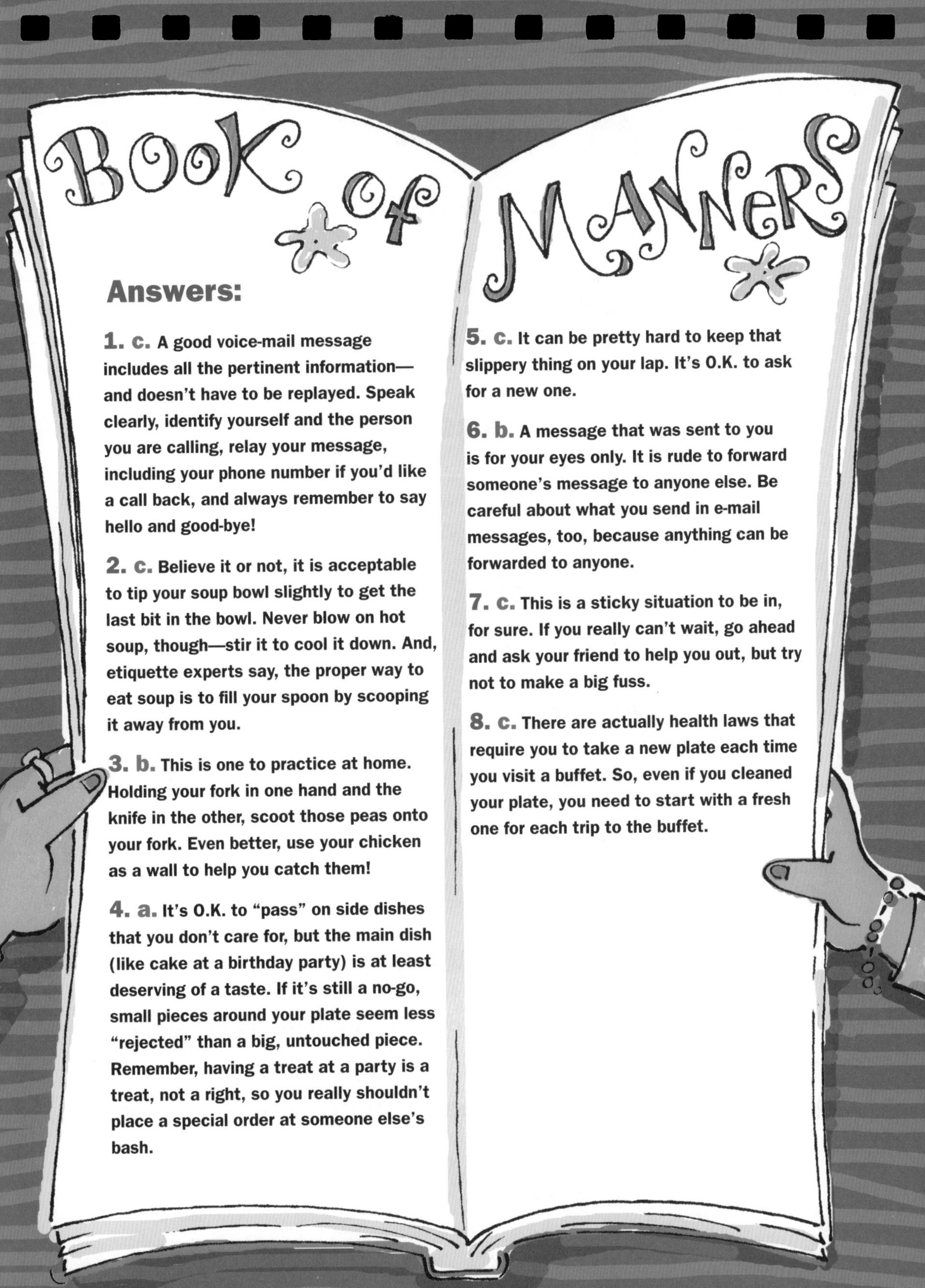

Answers:

1. c. A good voice-mail message includes all the pertinent information—and doesn't have to be replayed. Speak clearly, identify yourself and the person you are calling, relay your message, including your phone number if you'd like a call back, and always remember to say hello and good-bye!

2. c. Believe it or not, it is acceptable to tip your soup bowl slightly to get the last bit in the bowl. Never blow on hot soup, though—stir it to cool it down. And, etiquette experts say, the proper way to eat soup is to fill your spoon by scooping it away from you.

3. b. This is one to practice at home. Holding your fork in one hand and the knife in the other, scoot those peas onto your fork. Even better, use your chicken as a wall to help you catch them!

4. a. It's O.K. to "pass" on side dishes that you don't care for, but the main dish (like cake at a birthday party) is at least deserving of a taste. If it's still a no-go, small pieces around your plate seem less "rejected" than a big, untouched piece. Remember, having a treat at a party is a treat, not a right, so you really shouldn't place a special order at someone else's bash.

5. c. It can be pretty hard to keep that slippery thing on your lap. It's O.K. to ask for a new one.

6. b. A message that was sent to you is for your eyes only. It is rude to forward someone's message to anyone else. Be careful about what you send in e-mail messages, too, because anything can be forwarded to anyone.

7. c. This is a sticky situation to be in, for sure. If you really can't wait, go ahead and ask your friend to help you out, but try not to make a big fuss.

8. c. There are actually health laws that require you to take a new plate each time you visit a buffet. So, even if you cleaned your plate, you need to start with a fresh one for each trip to the buffet.

Happy Birthstone!

Do you **know your birthstone?** How about your best friend's? For each month, write in the traditional birthstone from the list below. Then turn the page to see what each stone means.

Months

January	July ....
February	August ....
March	September ....
April	October ....
May	November ....
June	December ....

Birthstones

Ruby

Opal

Turquoise

Topaz

Peridot

Emerald

Diamond

Garnet

Amethyst

Pearl

Aquamarine

Sapphire

Answers

The meanings of birthstones trace back to stories, beliefs, and legends—some more than a thousand years old! Are they for real? Who knows? Read the answers and see what you think.

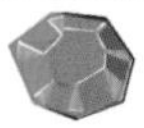

January
Garnet

The garnet symbolizes **confidence, grace,** and **loyalty,** and is thought to encourage friendships. Some believe wearing a garnet helps protect you from harm.

February
Amethyst

The amethyst symbolizes **love, sincerity,** and **honesty.** Legend says that wearing an amethyst can help calm your fears and keep you from excessiveness. Others believe an amethyst under your pillow brings pleasant dreams!

March
Aquamarine

"Aquamarine" is Latin for "sea water," so it's a perfect stone for anyone who loves the ocean. Some believe wearing an aquamarine could bring **love** and **affection.**

April
Diamond

The hardest stone, the diamond signifies **purity, strength,** and **love.** The diamond is considered the ultimate gift of love and is the most common stone in engagement rings.

May
Emerald

The emerald symbolizes **spring, hope,** and **peace.** If you looked at an emerald under a microscope, you would see tiny patterns that look like plants in a garden.

June
Pearl

Pearls represent **innocence, health,** and **wealth.** Pearls can also stand for **wisdom** or something precious. A pearl starts out as a tiny particle of sand in an oyster shell. Some pearls take up to three years to get large enough to be used in jewelry!

July
Ruby

The ruby represents **kindness, happiness,** and **honor.** In ancient times, people believed that rubies helped cure illnesses and patch up arguments.

August
Peridot

The peridot symbolizes **fame, honor,** and **protection.** Legends say pirates loved peridots. It was thought that wearing a peridot set in gold would prevent bad dreams and bring friendship, success, and good luck.

September
Sapphire

Sapphires stand for **wisdom, truth,** and **sincerity.** When you wear a sapphire, some say you might feel secure, brave, and strong.

October
Opal

Opals are a symbol of **hope, confi-dence,** and **innocence.** More than 500 years ago, during the Middle Ages, young blonde girls in Europe wore opals in their hair to protect its beautiful color. A good opal has the colors of all the other birthstones in it.

November
Topaz

Topaz represents **friendship, faithfulness,** and **honesty.** Some people believe wearing a topaz could bring friendship, fame, and fortune!

December
Turquoise

Turquoise symbolizes **happiness, good health, good luck,** and **success.** Giving or receiving a turquoise as a gift is like a pledge of friendship!

Are You an All-American Girl?

Take this quiz and see how much you know about **the good old U.S.A.!**

1. It's right before kickoff at your brother's football game. Everyone stands to sing the national anthem. What song is it?

a. **"America the Beautiful"**

b. **"The Star-Spangled Banner"**

c. **"Take Me Out to the Ball Game"**

d. **"My Country 'Tis of Thee"**

2. It's your job to draw the American flag for your group social studies project. For extra credit, you need to write a brief explanation of your work. Quick—what do the 13 stripes on the flag stand for?

a. **the 13th president of the United States**

b. **the 13 original colonies**

c. **the original 13 flavors of ice cream**

d. **the number of signatures on the Declaration of Independence**

3. Your gym teacher says you'll be practicing the "great American pastime" in your next gym class. What game are you getting pumped to play?

a. **baseball**

b. **football**

c. **soccer**

d. **kickball**

4. Your birthday card from Grandma arrived. She always includes a crisp $10 bill. Whose portrait are you expecting to find on the cash inside?

a. **Alexander Hamilton**

b. **Thomas Jefferson**

c. **Ronald Reagan**

d. **George Washington**

5. Your best friend lives in New York and you live in California. You have to tell her about what happened in school today, but you don't want to call too late. When it's 9 P.M. in California, what time is it in New York?

a. **9 P.M. What is this, a trick question?**

b. **6 P.M. She's probably just sitting down to dinner.**

c. **Midnight. You'd better wait until tomorrow to call.**

d. **11 P.M. It's two hours later there . . . but that's still too late to call.**

6. Your mom won the sales award at work, and her company gave her and Dad a trip to what is known as "The Youngest State." Where are they going? (Hint: It was the last state to enter the Union.)

a. **Alaska**

b. **Hawaii**

c. **Puerto Rico**

d. **Florida**

7. During summer break, your family is driving to South Dakota to see Mount Rushmore. What famous face do you NOT expect to see carved in stone?

a. George Washington

b. John F. Kennedy

c. Thomas Jefferson

d. Theodore Roosevelt

8. You signed up to help with the scenery for the school Thanksgiving play. You're in charge of painting the pilgrims' ship. What ship or ships brought pilgrims to America?

a. the *Susan Constant*

b. the *Mayflower*

c. the *Titanic*

d. the *Nina,* the *Pinta,* and the *Santa Maria*

9. Your mom adores Thai food and your dad loves Italian. But you prefer American fare. Which of these American foods was not actually invented in America? (HINT: More than one answer is correct!)

a. ice cream

b. hot dog

c. apple pie

d. French fries

e. pizza

f. bagels

Answers: 1. b 2. b 3. a 4. a 5. c 6. b 7. b (Abraham Lincoln is the fourth face.) **8. b 9. None** of them were actually invented in America . . . **a.** France **b.** Germany **c.** England **d.** Belgium **e.** Italy **f.** Germany

Send us your quiz ideas!

Have an idea for an awesome original quiz?
Got something you really want to know about yourself?

Tell us your best ideas for quizzes.
We just might . . .

a. **make another Quiz Book.**
b. **have fun reading your answers.**
c. **publish your quiz on our Web site.**

Write to us at
Quiz Book Editor
American Girl
P.O. Box 620998, 8400 Fairway Place
Middleton, WI 53562

or visit our Web site at www.americangirl.com.

Published by Pleasant Company Publications

Printed in China.
04 05 06 07 08 09 10 C&C 10 9 8 7 6 5 4 3 2 1

Editorial Development: Julie Williams, Michelle Watkins, and Sara Hunt
Art Direction and Design: Chris Lorette David
Consultant: Patricia K. Criswell, ACSW
Production: Kendra Pulvermacher, Mindy Rappe, Judith Lary, and Jeannette Bailey

Quiz on p. 68–69 based on information courtesy of Alan R. Hirsch, M.D., from his book *What Flavor Is Your Personality?* (Naperville, IL: Sourcebooks, Inc. 2001).